BAR
QUIZ

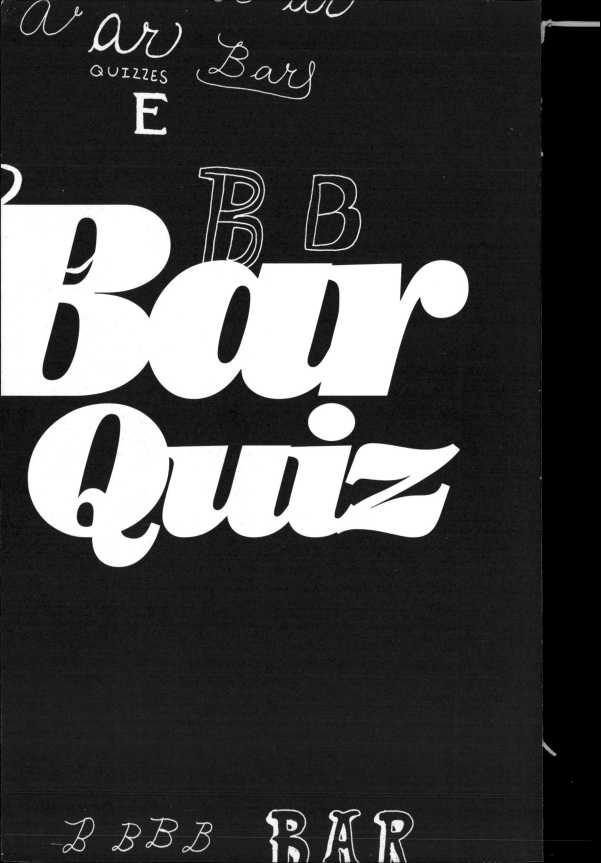

B B

a a

QU

by Rick
Saldin

STERLING INNOVATION
An imprint of Sterling Publishing Co., Inc.

New York / London
www.sterlingpublishing.com

STERLING, the Sterling logo, STERLING INNOVATION, and the Sterling Innovation logo are registered trademarks of Sterling Publishing Co., Inc.

10 9 8 7 6 5 4 3 2 1

Published by Sterling Publishing Co., Inc.
387 Park Avenue South, New York, NY 10016
© 2010 by Sterling Publishing Co., Inc.

Distributed in Canada by Sterling Publishing
c/o Canadian Manda Group, 165 Dufferin Street
Toronto, Ontario, Canada M6K 3H6
Distributed in the United Kingdom by GMC Distribution Services
Castle Place, 166 High Street, Lewes, East Sussex, England BN7 1XU
Distributed in Australia by Capricorn Link (Australia) Pty. Ltd.
P.O. Box 704, Windsor, NSW 2756, Australia

Sterling ISBN 978-1-4027-6953-5

For information about custom editions, special sales, premium and corporate purchases, please contact Sterling Special Sales Department at 800-805-5489 or specialsales@sterlingpublishing.com.

DEDICATION

To my friend and fellow Quizmaster, Tony Malokas, who got me involved with trivia, and to all the pub-goers that show up every Monday night at the Crown and Anchor Pub in Thousand Oaks for "the most fun you can have in the Conejo Valley on a Monday night."

Contents

OPEN

INTRO

When browsing in the bookstore, you'll find lots of trivia books, but you aren't likely to find one oriented toward the bar quiz crowd. All of the quizzes that you will find in this book were originally performed live in a bar environment. As you will see, the trivia is presented in a format that's perfect for the pub.

I've been writing and moderating bar quizzes for the last five years or so. During this time, I have amassed a vast collection of trivia books and assorted reference texts, but I believe that none of them specifically addresses the needs of the bar trivia aficionado, or in fact, the serious trivia hound. Trivia books are generally organized in a couple of very common ways. First, there is the "category" book, with lists of ten or fifteen questions per page all on one topic, such as "science," "sports," "nature," "literature," etc. Second, there are books arranged alphabetically with trivia facts. These are nice, I suppose, if you are looking for a particular factoid or just browsing through, but they aren't challenging, as they aren't presented as questions. Third, there are books patterned after popular game shows—generally starting with easy questions and getting progressively more difficult. Often the "easy" questions are so easy that any third grader would know the answer, and the "difficult" questions are so obscure and esoteric that very few adults are likely to know the answer.

I imagine that a number of you have never been to a bar quiz or even know of their existence. It turns out that bar quizzes, or pub quizzes, as they are also known, are a phenomenon that over time has swept the United Kingdom and, to a lesser degree, the United

States. In fact, it is likely that you would have a difficult time finding a town anywhere in England or Scotland where there isn't at least one pub that has a quiz night each week.

I began my sojourn into the world of the bar quiz in Monterey, California. If you have never been to Monterey, famous for John Steinbeck's *Cannery Row*, then you wouldn't know that the major industry there is tourism. And, apparently, tourists like to indulge in an adult beverage from time to time. The happening street downtown is Alvarado Street, which hosts no less than four different British pubs in about a half-mile stretch. Of course, where there is a British pub, there is generally a pub quiz. For those stout of heart, and perhaps liver, you can join a pub quiz Tuesday night at the London Bridge Pub or the Mucky Duck, and Thursday night at the Britannia Arms. I imagine the fourth pub, the Crown and Anchor, has decided there isn't a need for another night of trivia. By the way, if you like the quizzes in this book and you happen to be in Monterey, California, I recommend the quiz at the London Bridge on Tuesday nights. It is organized by my friend Big Tony, and is very similar in content and difficulty to those in this book.

Of course, no two bar quizzes are alike, and I've been to quite a few. In fact, if you are traveling and would like to find a quiz, you might check out this Web site: www.pubquizhelp.com. Here you will find a list of pub quizzes all over the country and abroad. My point is that I have a little experience with these quizzes, and by now I know what makes a good one.

In general, the bar quiz is run by the quizmaster who administers the quiz live. The best quizzes, I think, are actually created by the quizmaster presenting the quiz. If you look around you will discover that there is quite a cottage industry of "bar quizzes" that are sold to bar owners around the country. These consist generally of fifteen or more questions that are sent each week to the bar management. The questions tend to be generic and not particularly satisfying for the seriously hungry trivia hound.

How are my quizzes arranged, and what makes them different? First, each quiz is comprised of fifty questions. Generally, they take about ninety minutes to two hours to perform live, which makes for a good night out. The participants get a challenging evening, and the bar gets the patrons stuck in their seats eating and drinking for at least two hours—quite a coup for an otherwise quiet bar on a Tuesday or Wednesday night. Each quiz is designed to be challenging for four to six adults playing together, and the greatest challenge for the quizmaster is to create a quiz that is difficult, but not obscure. Ask a question that is too easy, and you open yourself up to some serious heckling from the crowd. With fifty to one hundred people playing, you obviously can't ask which planet is known for having the big red spot, and at the same time, you can't ask a question like, where did Marilyn Monroe go to high school? Who cares where Marilyn went to high school? (other than perhaps her prom date), and who could possibly know the answer? Ultimately, I like to provide a number of questions that are interesting; these are questions that people might bring up at the water cooler at work the next day. In my humble opinion, a good question is one in which at least one person in the bar has a good probability of knowing the answer.

Of course, you never know what people know, so that's part of the challenge: One person's easy question is another person's impossible question. Fortunately, each team generally has four or more players (I don't place a limit on the size of a team, but you might think about doing so in your bar), so it is usually very much a team effort. The difference between

"... you can't ask a question like, where did Marilyn Monroe go to high school?"

first, second, and third place is often just a question or two. For those individuals that say, "I don't know any trivia, or I'm not good at it," I always tell them that if they can provide just one answer that no one else on their team knows, they will prove to be the difference between winning and losing.

Each week, the quiz is presented in five sections of ten questions each. After a section is completed, I ask teams to trade papers with a nearby team and grade their answers. Occasionally, a section will have a theme, but the questions in the sections are broad based and cover a variety of topics. I tend to believe that organizing the sections by category is a bad idea. For instance, if I pose ten questions on sports, and there is no one on the team that is particularly strong in sports trivia, then the team might score zero on that section, which is bad for morale. That isn't to say that you can't have a lot of sports questions, if that's your preference, but I think you should spread them out throughout the quiz to make the effect less dramatic. So what about themes? Sometimes I will throw together ten questions that are subtly related to one another, which is fun for the patrons if they happen to catch on to the pattern early. They can use that knowledge to figure out answers that they wouldn't otherwise get. My friend Big Tony once put together a really nifty quiz section in which all the questions were in different categories, but the answers lined up as the last names of the first ten U.S. presidents. It was very effective. I tend to sprinkle the themes randomly, often going a month or more without doing one, so regular players don't get in the habit of looking for them. You will find a few of these themed sections in the bonus section in this book.

So, what's in store for you here? I've put together twenty-five quizzes of fifty questions each. Each has been performed live in a bar; however, I have taken the liberty of substituting a few questions when the original question required some specific knowledge of the community where the quiz was administered. In addition, there are twenty-five bonus quizzes.

Typically, the questions require a specific answer, but occasionally, for example, with a population question, I will give the participants a range that they must be within to get the question right, say, 10 percent. For the purposes of this book, I have not included many such ranges, but you should consider an answer "correct" if it is within 10 percent of the actual answer. On quiz night, you should be wary because sometimes the spread is designed to trick the participants. I also throw in an occasional true or false question, or a multiple-choice question, which adds a little variety and bumps up the scores. Generally, the winning team at one of my quizzes gets between 75 and 80 percent of the questions correct. My hope is that the worst team will still get approximately 45 percent of the questions correct—any less and I figure they won't come back.

If you are taking these quizzes alone, don't be surprised if your score is fairly low. Remember, the quizzes are designed for four to six adults combining their collective knowledge and experience.

At the back of the book you will find the bonus quizzes. The answers to the ten or more questions in each bonus section are all related. Occasionally, at the quiz, I offer up the bonus section because fifty questions just aren't enough. These bonus sections generally have some theme that is not outlined for the players. My emphasis with the bonus is to be creative and, hopefully, to entertain a little more. The bonus sections in this book are sometimes labeled with a theme and sometimes the theme is a mystery.

One reason I like the bonus sections for the live quiz is that occasionally the bonus section will elevate the score of a team that didn't do that well on the regular quiz. The bonus section has the added advantage of adding more points to the quiz, and the numbers dictate that the more points available, the less likely it is that a tie score will occur.

Best of luck! I hope you enjoy climbing this mountain of trivia and that once you reach the pinnacle, you have acquired a few interesting tidbits to entertain your family and friends.

QUIZZES

Q

one

QUIZ

PART A

---

1. Which capital city is farthest west: Berlin, Rome, Prague, or Vienna?

2. In which month do Canadians celebrate Thanksgiving?

3. In 2003, 24 states asked the movie industry to show less of what?

4. Yes or no: Has a guinea pig ever been launched into space?

5. What do the British call a traffic circle?

6. Which turns litmus paper blue: acids or bases?

7. What name is given to the act of trying to find water with a willow or hazel twig?

8. What two words are written on the yellow Lance Armstrong bracelets?

9. How many hurdles must be negotiated in the 100-meter hurdle race?

10. What band had a hit with the song "Accidentally in Love," and on what blockbuster movie soundtrack did it appear in 2004?

PART B

1. Rockhoppers, macaronis, and chinstraps are all what type of animal?

2. What is the maximum number of barrels that a brewery can produce in a year and still be considered a microbrewery?

3. Name the only director other than George Lucas that has directed both Carrie Fisher and Natalie Portman as of 2009.

4. Who had a #3 hit in 1966 with a song entitled "Secret Agent Man?"

5. What inventor nicknamed his kids "Dot" and "Dash?"

6. In 2006, Felipe Calderon held what office?

7. Which one of the following Shakespeare plays is not considered a tragedy: *Hamlet*, *Othello*, *Twelfth Night*, or *Macbeth*?

8. What is the largest visible granite rock in the world?

9. What was the first city in the Southern Hemisphere to host the Summer Olympics (in 1956)?

10. What was the name of Paul Bunyan's blue ox?

PART C

1. Which city is on Great Britain's west coast: Manchester, Liverpool, Leeds, or Birmingham?

2. *The Fellowship of the Ring* begins with Bilbo's birthday. How old is he?

3. In 1999, what band was named country group of the century by the Recording Industry Association of America (RIAA)?

4. What painter, most known for her flowers, has been suspected of making them look like female genitalia?

5. Adam Savage and Jamie Hyneman are collectively known on TV as what?

6. What is the nickname of the state of Nevada?

7. Neil Armstrong went to the moon's surface in the LEM: What do the letters in LEM stand for?

8. In the movie *History of the World: Part 1*, how many commandments did the Jehovah give the people to obey?

9. Albert Schweitzer was known as a great humanitarian, but did he ever win the Nobel Peace Prize?

10. Name five of the six documentaries directed by Michael Moore as of 2009.

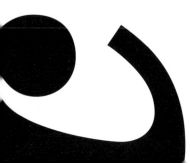

PART D

1. The beer Miller Chill was marketed as the beer with what two things?

2. What is the southernmost city on the continental United States?

3. How many bones are in the human wrist?

4. What kind of car did Louise drive in the movie *Thelma and Louise*?

5. In which Mexican state will you find Guadalajara: Vera Cruz, Sonora, or Jalisco?

6. Philip Roth wrote a book called *Portnoy's Complaint*. What was the complaint?

7. What team did Roger Clemens play for immediately before the Yankees?

8. What is the name of the clothing line by Prada that is directed at younger women?

9. According to the TV show's introductory theme, what was the Bionic Man's profession before he was injured?

10. Name the seven symbols located above the numbers 1–7 on a standard keyboard.

PART E

----

1. In the movie *E.T.: The Extra-Terrestrial*, E.T. eats Reese's Pieces, but what beer did he drink?

2. What two things make up the British dish "the toad in the hole?"

3. Name three baseball movies with Kevin Costner released between 1985 and 2000.

4. How many degrees off axis does the earth tilt?

5. What is the first line in *Hamlet?*

6. What two rap artists made cognac popular again with their song "Pass the Courvoisier?"

7. Which country lies on the tropic of Capricorn: Uruguay, Ecuador, Paraguay, or Bolivia?

8. What author penned *Wuthering Heights*?

9. What does the Dutch word *aardvark* translate to in English?

10. According to the well-known saying, what are the tools or handiwork of the Devil?

PART A

1. Dustin Hoffman won an Academy Award for his role in *Rain Man*. What was the other movie that he won a best actor Academy Award for?

2. In Egyptian mythology, who is the sister of Osiris and an underworld goddess?

3. What is used to speed up chemical reactions?

4. What term describes singing with no musical accompaniment?

5. Author of the *Divine Comedy*, what was Dante's last name?

6. What well-known product was advertised as "99 and 44/100%" pure?

7. What is the chemical symbol for fluorine?

8. What percent of U.S. states must ratify a constitutional amendment for it to become law?

9. Who was the other female sex symbol that starred with Marilyn Monroe in the movie *Gentlemen Prefer Blondes*?

10. In the first *The Chronicles of Narnia* movie, through what kind of portal do the characters travel to get to Narnia?

PART B

1. Which of these cities is farthest south in Florida: Jacksonville, Tampa, or Sarasota?

2. To what temperature in degrees Fahrenheit would you need to raise water in order to cause it to boil if you were at the summit of Mount Everest, i.e., 29,000 feet above sea level?

3. In the animal classification system, what order do humans belong to?

4. What was the first and last name of Shelley Long's character on the TV show *Cheers*?

5. Of the 43 million Hispanics in the United States (as of 2007), what percent is of Mexican origin?

6. When an acid and base react, what common compound other than water do you get?

7. The U.S. dollar is divided into one hundred pennies. What one hundred coins can the Euro be divided into?

8. The original name of what product was Dr. Bunting's Sunburn Remedy?

9. In the United States, we call 9-1-1 for emergencies. What numbers do the British use?

10. Who was the female lead in the Bob Hope and Bing Crosby road movies?

PART C

----

1. What is the name of the sea that separates Japan from the Koreas?

2. The most populous city in what state (population 533,000) was named after the most populous city in another state, which only has a population of 64,000?

3. In the movie *Scent of a Woman*, Al Pacino's character's favorite thing is, of course, women. What is "a close second?"

4. Named Vesta and Ceres, these are the two largest what that man has identified?

5. What music icon coined the term "power pop" in a 1966 British magazine?

6. What nickname is given to the followers of the music star Jimmy Buffett?

7. What was different about the basketballs used in the American Basketball Association, which merged with the NBA in 1976?

8. What was the name of Tarzan's chimpanzee?

9. Before committing a heinous act, who is best known for shouting, "sic semper Tyrannus," and who is credited with saying it first?

10. What day in the United States is celebrated as Flag Day?

PART D

1. State Route 46 near Cholame, California, is best known for what?

2. How many states border Indiana?

3. After what historical event did a reporter remark, "Oh, the humanity"?

4. What director was a passenger in the back of Robert De Niro's taxi in the movie *Taxi Driver*?

5. *People* magazine began their award for the Sexiest Man Alive in 1985 with what actor?

6. What was the nickname of the computer in the movie *Resident Evil*?

7. What well-known food company that owns brands such as Ore-Ida, Boston Market, and TGI Fridays also owns Weight Watchers?

8. Is the Rock of Gibraltar made mostly of limestone, basalt, or sandstone?

9. Cartoonist Garry Trudeau is married to what American television journalist?

10. Mount McKinley is located in what national park?

PART E

----

1. In the world of sports, their introduction goes as follows: "They are often imitated, they are never equaled, they are _____."

2. Who was the only U.S. president whose first language was not English?

3. How many times did the New York Yankees win the World Series in the twentieth century?

4. In 1928, the Fleer Company introduced this chewy product.

5. "My country 'tis of thee, sweet land of liberty, of thee I sing. Land where my fathers died...." What is the next line?

6. What rock star had a hit with a song that begins, "I was a little too tall, could've used a few pounds"?

7. What principle in science states that observable quantities such as energy and time or position and momentum cannot be measured with complete accuracy simultaneously?

8. On the American version of *Who Wants to Be a Millionaire*, by what method do contestants qualify to get into the "hot seat"?

9. If you multiply the base times the height and divide by two, you will get the area of what?

10. The capital of what island nation is Suva?

QUIZ three

PART A

1. In chess, the king is surrounded by the queen, pawns, and what other piece?

2. Whose cow supposedly started the Great Chicago Fire?

3. How many numbered squares are on a bingo card?

4. In which two South American countries will you find a city called Santa Cruz?

5. *Do Androids Dream of Electric Sheep?* is the story that what film is based on?

6. On average, which is colder: the North or South Pole?

7. What actor, best known for a sci-fi role, recorded a 1991 album called *Ol' Yellow Eyes Is Back?*

8. What is the letter and number designation of the U.S. stealth fighter?

9. Is the Nile River closer to 4,000, 5,000, or 6,000 miles long?

10. What makes the White Cliffs of Dover white?

PART B

----

1. In what year was the Great Chicago Fire?

2. Prior to World War II, Twinkies had a different filling. What was the filling?

3. Who crowned Napoleon Bonaparte as emperor?

4. What do the letters VSOP stand for on a bottle of Cognac?

5. What company's logo features a black colt on a yellow background?

6. *Pterodactyl* is Greek for what two words? What type of animal does it describe?

7. What king of France was husband to Marie Antoinette?

8. What is Elvis Presley's middle name?

9. What color is primrose?

10. What is the name for a group of ponies?

PART C

----

1. By what nickname did Louis Gossett, Jr.'s character refer to Richard Gere's character in the movie *An Officer and a Gentleman*?

2. What are the two countries in which you could find mountains known as the Dolomites?

3. The first line of what children's movie is, "If you want to find Cherry Tree Lane, all you have to do is ask a policeman at the crossroads"?

4. In what city was Anne Frank hiding when the Nazis captured her?

5. What is the name of the supercomputer that waged war against humans in the *Terminator* movies?

6. What two countries fought the Opium War in 1839?

7. Specifically in the United States, what symbol is used to denote an intermediate ski trail?

8. Name the three bones of the middle ear.

9. What were the last names of Bonnie and Clyde?

10. How long after the first time that U.S. astronauts set foot on the moon did we do it again on another mission?

PART D

----

1. What is the name of the hospital in the TV series *Grey's Anatomy*?

2. Who wrote the score for the movie *Star Wars*?

3. What town was the setting for Nathaniel Hawthorne's *House of the Seven Gables*?

4. What body of water does the Danube River flow into?

5. Who invented the pistol known as the "hideaway gun"?

6. What building is on the back of the U.S. $10 bill?

7. The song "All that Jazz" comes from what musical?

8. What U.S. president established the Peace Corps?

9. Rocker Peter Criss is best known for wearing what on stage?

10. From what country do the Pennsylvania Dutch trace their origins?

PART E

1. In the poker game Omaha, how many cards is each player dealt?

2. What European city was originally two cities separated by the Danube River?

3. What U.S. state has the capital city with the highest elevation?

4. *The Canterbury Tales* are a representation of English society during what century?

5. If you need a surgery called a rhinoplasty, what body part will be affected?

6. Who wrote the novel *Cannery Row*?

7. Christmas Island is part of what country?

8. What was the last year that the Dodgers won the World Series (as of 2009)?

9. In the movie *Alien,* what was the pet cat's name?

10. Six flags have flown over Texas—name them.

PART A

1. What is the capital of Switzerland?

2. Name a month that has the star sign of Cancer.

3. Of the U.S. states whose names begin with an *A*, only one ends in a different letter. Name that state.

4. How long does a nanosecond last?

5. What law states that at a constant temperature the pressure of a gas is inversely proportional to its volume?

6. How much silver must an item contain to be considered sterling silver?

7. What is Divine Brown best known for?

8. Who was the British king when the colonies declared independence?

9. John Carpenter was the first person on the American version of *Who Wants to Be a Millionaire* to win $1 million. What was his stated profession?

10. At what sport can you see nose walking?

PART B

----

1. Who said, "If you want to know the value of money, try to borrow some"?

2. When did the Panama Canal open?

3. What animal always gives birth to identical quadruplets?

4. What is the name of the acid in vinegar?

5. What country is surrounded by Columbia and Peru?

6. How many gallons are in a barrel of oil?

7. What comedy movie's original working title was *Jesus Christ, Lust of Glory*?

8. What do the letters ROTC stand for?

9. Whose last meal consisted purportedly of four scoops of ice cream and six chocolate chip cookies?

10. What was the nickname of the plane piloted by Major Charles Sweeney that bombed Nagasaki?

PART C

1. What is the common name of the anatomical juxtaposition of two orbicularis oris muscles in a state of contraction?

2. Who was the first Bond girl?

3. Whose home run record did Mark McGuire break with his 62nd home run?

4. The Parthenon is the better known name for the temple of whom?

5. What do the J and the K stand for in author J.K. Rowling's name?

6. Diamonds are the hardest substance. What is the softest?

7. In which opera is the Toreador song featured?

8. Yes or no: Film critic Roger Ebert has won the Pulitzer Prize.

9. In what decade did the federal minimum wage reach a dollar?

10. What was the first European country to ban smoking in bars?

PART D

----

1. What is the name of the instrument used to measure the speed of the greens in the game of golf?

2. Which U.S. president said, "Never let us negotiate out of fear, but never let us fear to negotiate"?

3. What kind of nymph is a dryad?

4. What is the largest inland water mass in the United Kingdom?

5. Which crime fighter has the power to cloud men's minds?

6. What style of art did Pablo Picasso help start?

7. What boxer originated the phrase, "He can run, but he can't hide"?

8. Aspirin was originally obtained from the bark of what tree?

9. What three-word code phrase was used by the Japanese to signal the attack on Pearl Harbor?

10. How many passengers were on the *Mayflower?*

PART E

----

1. What did Rumpelstiltskin want in exchange for teaching the miller's daughter how to spin gold from straw?

2. The Cook Strait separates what two areas of land?

3. In what year was the famous Woodstock festival held?

4. What do panphobics fear?

5. Who was Gene Kelly's unusual dance partner in the movie *Anchors Aweigh*?

6. What bird is traditionally thought to sing before it dies?

7. What was the name of Buddy Holly's band?

8. Who introduced the term *mole* to describe a spy in his novel *Tinker, Tailor, Soldier, Spy*.

9. From what Broadway musical comes the song "76 Trombones"?

10. What is a penny-farthing?

QUIZ

five

5

PART A

1. What is the capital of Panama?

2. Humpty Dumpty sat on a wall. What was Humpty Dumpty?

3. What three things make up the drink called a mudslide?

4. Which came first: the yo-yo, the jigsaw puzzle, or the Raggedy Ann doll?

5. In *Peter Pan*, how did Captain Hook lose his hand?

6. What is the name of the actor that played James Bond in the 2006 *Casino Royale*?

7. Yes or no: Michael Douglas is older than Catherine Zeta Jones' father?

8. What was the first cable network in the United States?

9. CH_4 is the chemical symbol for what gas?

10. As the weight on the end of a pendulum increases, how does the time it takes to swing from one side to the other change?

PART B

---

1. Which 1952 John Steinbeck novel became a best seller again in 2003, when Oprah selected it for her book club?

2. What organization is perhaps best known for distributing bibles in hotels?

3. What type of celestial body's name means *wanderer* in Greek?

4. The United States is #1 in Tabasco sauce consumption. What country is #2?

5. What U.S. coin went into circulation on August 1, 1932?

6. If you commit the crime of regicide, who are you killing?

7. Name the classical music term that describes a sad night piece.

8. In the song "The Devil Went Down to Georgia," what is Johnny's prize?

9. What writer's mystery novels are all set in Santa Teresa, California?

10. Krakatoa is a famous volcanic island that is part of what country?

PART C

1. What name is given to a number whose factors add up to the number, such as the number 28?

2. Which came first: McDonald's or White Castle?

3. Which organ in the body destroys old red blood cells?

4. What mythical creature was featured on Uma Thurman's boots in *Kill Bill: Vol. 2*?

5. The Hope Diamond was once part of what country's crown jewels?

6. How many yards is a furlong?

7. What famous antiquity will you find in Salisbury Plain?

8. You often see dates followed by BC or AD, and occasionally you see BCE. What do those letters stand for?

9. True or false? The state of Idaho borders Canada.

10. Name the six smallest European countries that are not islands.

PART D

1. What island was made famous by Gauguin's paintings?

2. This small animal's name means "first animal."

3. In *Star Wars,* which character built C3PO?

4. What is the official language of Kenya?

5. What was Babe Ruth's real first name?

6. Who is the only U.S. president to utter the line, "Live from New York, it's Saturday Night!" on the air?

7. How many years must you be a U.S. citizen before you can be a member of the senate?

8. True or false? If the mom has blood type A, and the baby has blood type O, then the dad must have blood type O.

9. How much water in gallons can the average camel store in its hump?

10. What is the only walled city in North America?

PART E

----

1. What is unusual about the Manx cat?

2. What blonde bombshell was the first "Tool Time" girl on TV's *Home Improvement?*

3. In fencing, what is the only weapon whose edge as well as its point can be used for a touch?

4. Seven U.S. states have this bird as their state bird.

5. What mythical figure does cartoon character Linus Van Pelt wait for each year?

6. What was the last year that man walked on the moon?

7. From which Shakespearean play do we get the phrase, "There's something rotten in Denmark?"

8. From the window on what floor of the book depository was JFK supposedly shot?

9. What film was the most expensive to make in the twentieth century?

10. Name the four moons in our solar system that are larger than our moon.

Q

six

QUIZ

PART A

1. What is the capital of Malaysia?

2. Movies like *Jurassic Park* use CGI: What does CGI stand for?

3. According to the proverb, what is the spice of life?

4. The Sun Trust Bank in Atlanta is home to the secret recipe of what?

5. What was Julia Roberts' next movie after *Pretty Woman*?

6. Little Miss Muffet ate her curds and whey. What is whey?

7. What is the #1 export of Hawaii?

8. True or false? The medical term for the name of the pain you get when you eat something cold too fast is an ice cream headache?

9. In pool, how many balls are used in the game of Eight-ball?

10. Who composed the "Semper Fidelis" march for the Marines?

PART B

----

1. Which one of these countries doesn't contain any part of the Andes Mountains: Chile, Venezuela, Uruguay, or Argentina?

2. American Indians became citizens of the United States when Congress recognized them in what year?

3. Who wrote the book *Lady Chatterley's Lover*?

4. What was the first drug created by recombinant DNA technology?

5. In what decade was the jitterbug a fad?

6. Who was the only U.S. president to serve nonconsecutive terms as president?

7. What country is closest to the point of 0 latitude and 0 longitude?

8. In computers, what do the letters in BIOS stand for?

9. Which two hopefuls participated in the first televised presidential debate?

10. As of 2008, how many #1 hits has Bruce Springsteen had in the United States?

PART C

1. In the movie *Top Gun,* Tom Cruise sings to Kelly McGillis. Name the song and the artists that recorded it.

2. What author's novels were the basis for the futuristic movies *Total Recall* and *Minority Report*?

3. In what U.S. state will you find the Blue Ridge Mountains?

4. If you are xenophobic, what are you afraid of?

5. Who is actress Blythe Danner's famous actress daughter?

6. What paper did Clark Kent write for?

7. Who wrote the "The Firebird"?

8. What do the letters BRB stand for in instant message speak?

9. What two cities does the Iditarod Great Sled Race go between?

10. Alaska and Hawaii entered the union after 1900. Name the other three states that also did this.

PART D

1. True or false? The black mamba snake is actually black.

2. What name is used to describe when all the money bet on an event is placed in a pool and the amounts bet determine the various odds?

3. Who is the Egyptian god of the sun?

4. Who commanded the regiment known as the Green Mountain Boys?

5. What street is purportedly the curviest street in the world?

6. The 38th parallel is best known for separating what?

7. By what name is the disease Creutzfeldt-Jakob better known?

8. By what nickname is Albert DeSalvo better known?

9. Name the five movies that the Beatles did.

10. "Where the world's best athletes prove it" is the motto of what sporting event?

PART E

1. In human terms, how old is a dog of five years?

2. By what name is Edison Arantes do Nascimento better known?

3. True or false? The painting of the *Mona Lisa* has no eyebrows.

4. What classic comedy movie popularized the line, "Joey, do you like movies about gladiators?"

5. On TV medical shows you often hear them say something like, "Start an IV with D5W." The W is for water. What is the D for?

6. What was the name of the ship that eventually came to the rescue of the *Titanic*?

7. What is the name of the famous porn star that we later learned started her career at age fifteen?

8. Which author wrote a novel with a character named Holly Golightly?

9. What term is used to describe laws that regulate moral behavior such as the sale of alcohol on Sundays?

10. Totaling nearly 3 million acres, what California county is the largest in the country?

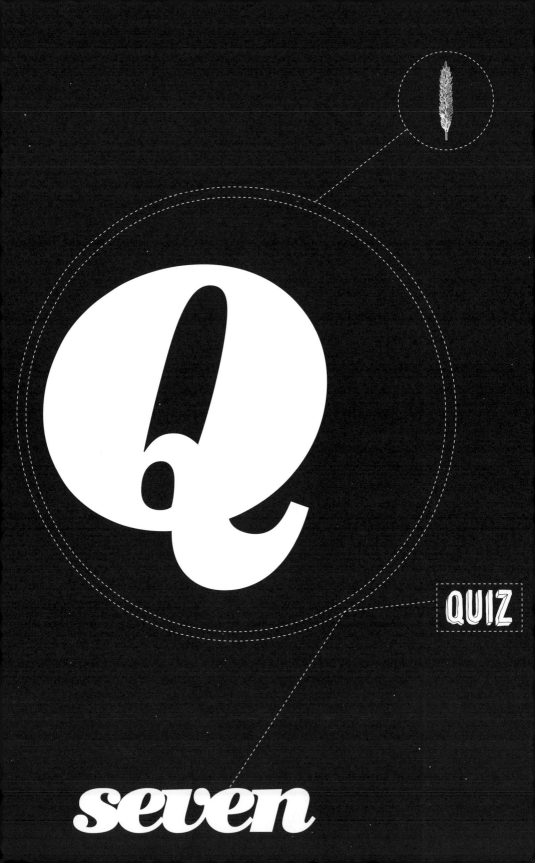

QUIZ

seven

PART A

----

1. What is the capital of Alabama?

2. How did Joan of Arc die?

3. What was the name of Bob Marley's backup band?

4. What is the technical name for the collarbone?

5. If you order coq au vin, what kind of food will you get?

6. True or false? As of January 1, 2008, Tiger Woods has been ranked as #1 in the official world golf rankings for all of the twenty-first century.

7. What philosopher is known for saying, *"Cogito ergo sum"*?

8. In what movie will you find John Travolta wearing a T-shirt of the U.C. Santa Cruz Banana Slugs?

9. Which amendment to the U.S. constitution protects against double jeopardy?

10. Who became president when JFK died?

PART B

1. Art Fleming was the original host of what TV game show?

2. For whom was the bell tolling when the Liberty Bell cracked?

3. Who was the *Saturday Night Live* actor who used the catch phrase, "That's the ticket?"

4. As a professional, Muhammad Ali lost five professional fights, one was against Trevor Berbick. Name the other four opponents.

5. True or false? Roger Moore as 007 never says, "Vodka martini, shaken not stirred."

6. Complete the following saying that President Woodrow Wilson's vice president, Thomas Marshall, is known for: "What this country needs is a good. . ."

7. What country is Mount Kilimanjaro in?

8. What breed of dog is Scooby Doo?

9. What female TV star was on the cover of the first *TV Guide*?

10. What is the chemical symbol for gold?

PART C

----

1. What chemical is used to preserve anatomic specimens?

2. What is the name of the fictional character whose picture appears on the label of Columbian coffee?

3. Who was the first man defeated in a U.S. presidential race (in 1789)?

4. The Romans called this goddess Minerva; what did the Greeks call her?

5. Skier Vinko Bogataj has one claim to fame, and it has been shown frequently on TV. What is it?

6. What is the name of the president of the World Bank who was found guilty of getting his girlfriend a high-paying job?

7. What is the highest denomination of U.S. coin?

8. What is the capital city of Canada?

9. What famous author wrote the *Foundation* trilogy?

10. Name the four U.S. states that are technically not states, but commonwealths.

PART D

1. What sport takes place at the "Brickyard"?

2. What artist is known for painting water lilies in his garden at Giverny?

3. True or false? The state bird of Florida is the flamingo.

4. Which one of these cities can be found on the Rhine River: Stuttgart, Cologne, or Frankfurt?

5. Who was the first woman athlete to be named athlete of the year by *Sports Illustrated* magazine?

6. In the binary system, how is the number three represented?

7. Silicon dioxide is the chemical name of what everyday item found in most homes?

8. How many states are in the country of Mexico?

9. Which religious group is also known as The Society of Friends?

10. Provide the Latin translation for "Out of many, one."

PART E

1. Who was Alexander the Great's tutor?

2. Smith, Vassar, and Wellesley are members of a larger group of colleges collectively known as what?

3. Who is Robert Zimmerman better known as?

4. Where in the body will you find the lachrymal glands?

5. In what country was the *Titanic* built?

6. If you order a dish in England with sultanas, what will you get?

7. Who wrote *The Legend of Sleepy Hollow*?

8. A bottle labeled "drink me" is a pivotal feature in what literary work?

9. What is the collective name for the group of gases that includes helium and neon?

10. In 1943, her legs were insured by Lloyds of London for $1 million.

QUIZ

eight

PART A

1. What is the capital of Columbia?

2. True or false? Ben Franklin signed both the Declaration of Independence and the U.S. Constitution.

3. Camels do not store water in their humps, so where do they store it?

4. Which physiologist penned a treatise titled *Conditioned Reflexes*?

5. Where is the world court, officially known as the International Court of Justice, located?

6. In the game of horseshoes, how many points do you get for a ringer?

7. What color is a twenty dollar bill in the game of Monopoly?

8. In mythology, who or what poses the riddle, "What creature walks on four legs in the morning, two at noon, and three in the evening?"

9. At whose ranch did Elizabeth Taylor marry Larry Fortenski?

10. The first five members of the National Baseball Hall of Fame included Walter Johnson and Christie Mathewson. Who were the other three?

PART B

----

1. In the United Kingdom, they have a candy bar called the Mars bar. By what name do we call the same candy bar in the United States?

2. In a mile run, if you have run three-quarters of the way, how many yards do you have left?

3. In the book and the movie *The Perfect Storm,* from what state does the *Andrea Gail* sail from?

4. Who said, "Old soldiers never die, they just fade away?"

5. In what country was the first under-four-minute mile actually run?

6. In the Otis Redding song "Dock on the Bay," how many miles did he roam?

7. What foreign country's capital was named after the fifth U.S. president?

8. What sea is located immediately north of Iran?

9. What school did the screw-ups in *National Lampoon's Animal House* attend?

10. Which U.S. state's border is entirely water, with the exception of fifty miles?

PART C

----

1. Who was on the cover of the first *Rolling Stone* magazine?

2. How many bedrooms are in the game of Clue?

3. What actor portrayed God in the movie *Bruce Almighty?*

4. In what sport do the participants use crampons?

5. Other than chicory for flavor, what is added to coffee to make a Thai iced coffee (do not answer ice)?

6. Which comes after the stomach, the large intestine or the small intestine?

7. What country experienced the Velvet Revolution?

8. Sally Ride was the youngest American to do what?

9. Elizabeth Hurley endorsed the perfume products called Beautiful and Pleasures for what cosmetics company?

10. Grace Kelly made two films, *Countrygirl* and *High Society,* with what leading man?

PART D

1. Mars, Inc. renamed the American version of the British Mars bar what?

2. Jeanne Butler was the lesser known half of the duo that brought what dance sensation to the United States?

3. True or false? Every U.S. president that wore a beard while in office was a republican.

4. What was the name of the sequel to Michael Crichton's novel *Jurassic Park*?

5. What did Dr. John Pemberton invent in 1886?

6. When it comes to turkey gobbling, is it the males, the females, or both that gobble?

7. Two men have been named *People* magazine's Sexiest Man Alive twice. Name them.

8. What engineer is commonly associated with building the first steamboat?

9. Name the five longest rivers in the United States.

10. If you are in the doctor's office in Great Britain and you are complaining of "piles," what are you complaining of?

PART E

1. The Black September terrorist group is infamous for what 1972 event?

2. Chesapeake Bay is formed by what two states?

3. What famous person wrote under the pseudonym of Richard Saunders?

4. Who was Enola Gay?

5. What state capital will you find adjacent to the Salt River?

6. Within 500 miles, how much shorter a distance is it to go through the Panama Canal than around South America?

7. What is the oldest licensed distillery in the world?

8. What relatively old singer released a solo album in June 2007 called *Memory Almost Full*?

9. Whose motto is *semper paratus?*

10. Name the eight Ivy League schools.

nine

PART A

1. What is the capital of North Dakota?

2. What is the birthstone for the month of May?

3. Nike is the goddess of what?

4. True or false? Mel Blanc, the voice of Bugs Bunny, was allergic to carrots.

5. How many numbers are on a Keno board?

6. What is the chemical symbol for boron?

7. Scientist Alexander Fleming is known for discovering what life saver?

8. What city is located directly across the river from Juarez, Mexico?

9. What is Itzhak Perlman best known for?

10. What is the only position on the field that is not named in the "Who's on first?" skit by Abbott and Costello?

PART B

----

1. The first line of what book begins, "A few miles south of Soledad, the Salinas River drops in close to the hillside bank, and runs deep and green?"

2. What classic science-fiction movie is based on the Arthur C. Clarke novel *Sentinel?*

3. In Big Sur, California, there is a restaurant called Nepenthe. It is named after a magic drink that was supposed to do what?

4. In what state will you find Lassen Volcanic National Park?

5. Who played Scarlett O'Hara in the movie *Gone with the Wind?*

6. By what names are the two numbers in a blood pressure reading known?

7. What two actors were partners in TV's *Blue Moon Detective Agency*?

8. In World War II there was a group of people known as WASPs. What do the letters in WASP stand for?

9. Which U.S. president took the oath of office in a private cabin within Air Force One?

10. What is the largest island in the West Indies?

PART C

1. As of January 2008, the Summer Olympics have been hosted by only three U.S. cities; name them.

2. In craps, what number is nicknamed "centerfield"?

3. What was the actual business that the Wright Brothers were in when they made their historic flight?

4. What actress played Walter Matthau and Jack Lemmon's love interest in the movie *Grumpy Old Men?*

5. Who was the U.S. president when the Panama Canal was completed?

6. What song was the first solo effort by a Beatle to reach #1?

7. Who was the British prime minister immediately before Margaret Thatcher?

8. How many liters is in a magnum of champagne?

9. Gunmetal is an alloy of what three metals?

10. Who wrote the novel *Finnegan's Wake*?

PART D

1. Both preserves and marmalade have pieces of fruit in them, so what is found in marmalade that is not also in preserves?

2. What name is given to the privilege granted to certain elected officials allowing them to send mail for free?

3. What rock band had a hit with a song that begins with the lines, "You know that it would be untrue, you know that I would be a liar"?

4. True or false? The Stone Mountain sculpture was started by the same man that sculpted Mount Rushmore.

5. What is the only country name used in the NATO phonetic alphabet (international radio spelling alphabet)?

6. Who did the music for *West Side Story*?

7. Which Hawaiian island is nicknamed the "Garden Island"?

8. Which radio personality claims to "have talent, on loan from God?"

9. In the movie *Point of No Return*, Bridget Fonda's character is obsessed with the music of what jazz and blues singer?

10. In what city's art institute will you find Grant Wood's painting *American Gothic*?

PART E

1. In what city is the National Finals Rodeo held each December?

2. In meters-per-second squared, what is the acceleration rate of gravity for an object in free fall?

3. In what country will you find the town of Pilsen, which is famous for its beer?

4. Three Mile Island, home to a nuclear accident, is in what state?

5. What were the two first names of the Siamese twins that gave rise to the name "Siamese twins"?

6. In what state would you purportedly find the Lost Dutchman Mine?

7. Which city is closest to the capital of Australia: Perth, Melbourne, or Sydney?

8. From what country did the U.S. purchase the Virgin Islands?

9. What bone will you find at the base of the human spine?

10. Telly Savalas played Kojak on TV. What was Kojak's first name?

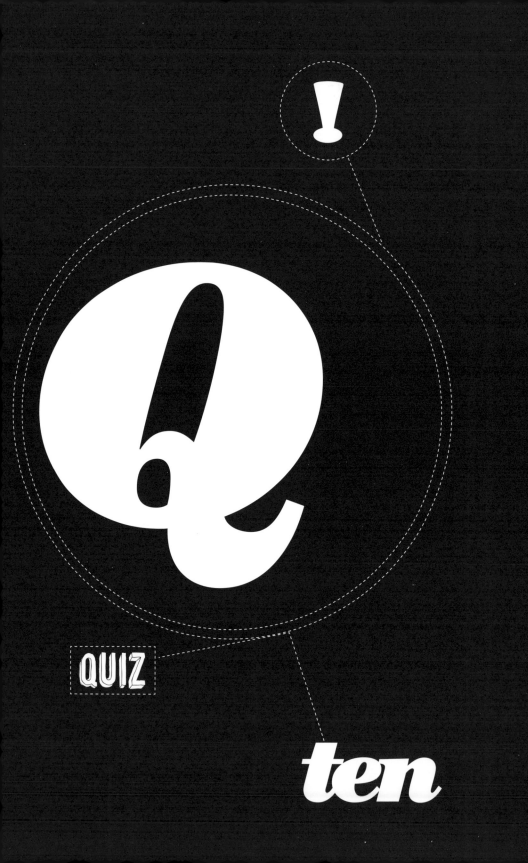

PART A

1. What do we call the country of Ceylon now?

2. What meat is traditionally used in the dish ossobuco?

3. Who is Hollywood's most famous costume designer?

4. Is rhubarb a fruit or a vegetable?

5. How many horses have won the Kentucky Derby twice?

6. Which company's first slogan was: "You push the button, we do the rest"?

7. True or false? The equator passes through the Galapagos Islands.

8. Where would a Scotsman wear his Tam O'Shanter?

9. In what hotel in Las Vegas was the World Series of Poker held prior to its move to the Rio Hotel?

10. Who erroneously predicted in a speech that "the world will little note, nor long remember, what we say here today"?

PART B

----

1. In what country will you find Copacabana Beach?

2. Which president signed the Smithsonian Institute into existence?

3. What artery leaves the right ventricle in humans?

4. Is a walrus a carnivore or a vegetarian?

5. What astrological sign falls between Scorpio and Capricorn?

6. Who was it that said, "Friends, Romans, countrymen, lend me your ears?"

7. In what year did the Beatles break up?

8. Which is the collective noun for a bunch of jellyfish: a smack, a dray, or a bard?

9. Singing brothers Zac, Taylor, and Isaac are better known as?

10. Common in poetry, what term is used to describe the repetition of an initial consonant sound in two or more words in a line?

PART C

1. The Labrador Sea separates North America from where?

2. It is known as the scent of the 1960s.

3. What is the name of the circus organ that is operated by a keyboard and has steam whistles?

4. What is the name of the character that led a double life as Zorro?

5. Interstate I-90 leaves Seattle and ends in what city?

6. What art form did Alexander Calder create in 1930?

7. In what medium did artist Rene Lalique work?

8. In what film does Julia Roberts' character fake her own death to escape domestic violence?

9. What is Harland Sanders famous for?

10. In the movie *Star Trek: The Voyage Home*, the symbol of the Cetacean Institute is actually the logo of what California attraction?

PART D

1. What hotel chain takes its name from the Spanish word for "resting place"?

2. What comedy team has appeared in the most movies together?

3. What seventeenth century English poet wrote a poem about his own blindness?

4. What actor played the president in the movie *Nixon*?

5. What cocktail consists of a lump of sugar, two dashes of bitters, two ounces of whiskey, a lemon peel, an orange wedge, and a cherry?

6. What mathematical constant is approximately equal to 2.71821?

7. The gas N_2O is known by what nickname?

8. From what country do we get Edam cheese?

9. To what group of elements do beryllium, magnesium, and calcium belong?

10. The Queensberry rules are associated with what activity?

PART E

----

1. What is the name of the stock that Martha Stewart was accused of insider trading with?

2. By what name is the Israeli secret service known?

3. Which Broadway musical features the song "There's No Business Like Show Business?"

4. A drug overdose led to what actor's death at the Viper Room in 1993?

5. What famous actor received the Academy Award for Best Actor for his performance in the movie *It Happened One Night?*

6. If you have an excess of uric acid in your blood, you most likely suffer from what ailment?

7. In tennis, what is the name of the tournament where nations send teams to compete (not the Olympics)?

8. Which one of these would you associate with Barcelona, Spain: the Atlantic Ocean, the Bay of Biscay, or the Mediterranean Sea?

9. What is the name of the Spanish chilled soup made with tomatoes and garlic?

10. What is dendrochronology?

PART A

1. Rabat is the capital of what country?

2. What two sets of muscles are used in breathing?

3. Who recorded the album *The Rise and Fall of Ziggy Stardust*?

4. What is the name of the sea witch in *The Little Mermaid*?

5. Which is the farthest planet visible to the unaided eye?

6. Yes or no: Is rice paper made from rice?

7. What do the letters in BMW stand for?

8. What animal do you get if you cross an American buffalo with cattle?

9. What year was the great San Francisco earthquake?

10. According to legend, by what animals were Romulus and Remus nourished?

PART B

----

1. From what country do we get Limburger cheese?

2. What cartoon characters lived in Frostbite Falls?

3. What is the length of the Appalachian Trail in miles?

4. On a motorcycle, what is the pillion?

5. What is the monetary unit of Portugal?

6. What is meant by the old English Navy phrase "splice the mainbrace?"

7. In inches, how much rainfall must occur in an area for it to be considered a rainforest?

8. The Strait of Messina separates what two areas of land?

9. What important British document was issued in 1215 AD?

10. To which tribe did Geronimo belong?

PART C

----

1. What is the more formal name for the ritual suicide called hara-kiri?

2. In what city will you find the Spanish Steps?

3. What actor said, "A lot of people have asked me how short I am—since my last divorce, I think I'm about $100,000 short"?

4. What is the name of the large body of water between Quebec and the Northwest Territory?

5. Way back in the day, how many pennies were there in a shilling?

6. Also way back in the day, what type of torture would you be subjected to if you were racked?

7. What is the main spice in the Hungarian dish of goulash?

8. What is the chemical name for aspirin?

9. Name the two people that appear naked on the cover of the album *Unfinished Music No. 1: The Two Virgins*?

10. Name the four nucleotides that make up DNA.

PART D

1. On what river will you find the city of Liverpool?

2. What blood vessel returns blood from the head to the heart?

3. Who was the first English sea captain to sail around the world?

4. Which U.S. state shares a border with both North and South Carolina?

5. From what fruit is the drink called slivovitz made?

6. What do we call the island of Formosa now?

7. Who was the commander of Hitler's *Luftwaffe?*

8. What name is given to the triangular cut of diamond?

9. What Chinese game swept the United States as a craze in 1922?

10. What five events make up the modern pentathlon?

PART E

1. In the *Matrix* movies, what is the name of the home of the humans?

2. What song was the Rolling Stones' first number one hit in the United States?

3. What name is given to the study and practice of the rules of classification of living and extinct organisms?

4. Who was the first U.S. president not officially born a British citizen (i.e., born after 1776)?

5. Central Park is three blocks wide; within one mile, how long is it?

6. With which musical group is Syd Vicious associated?

7. How many hours difference is there between Alaska's time zone and California's?

8. What city known for gambling has the nickname "the world's playground"?

9. Who was the leader of the Greeks in the Trojan War?

10. By manufacturer, which one of the following doesn't belong in the list: Grape-Nuts, Frosted Flakes, Rice Krispies, or Fruit Loops?

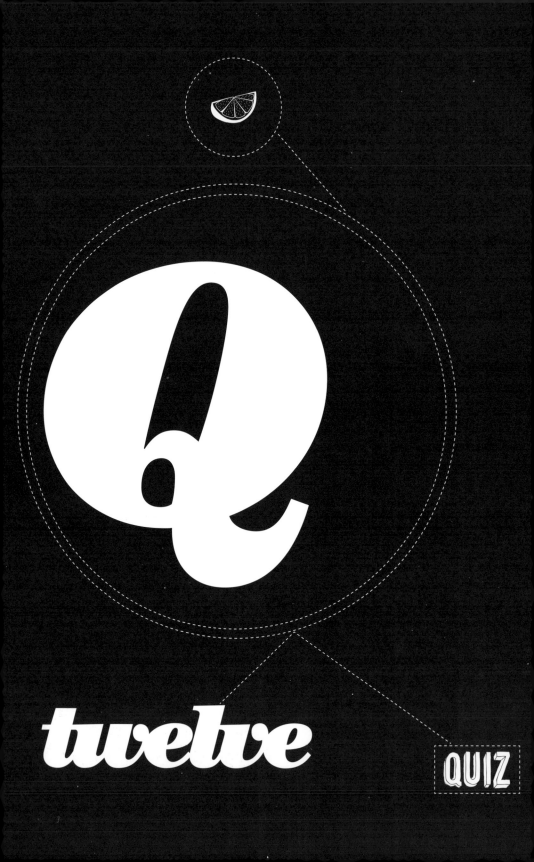

PART A

1. What is the capital of Wisconsin?

2. One, two, buckle my shoe; three, four, knock at the door; five, six, pick up sticks; seven, eight, _____?

3. How many times was FDR elected President of the United States?

4. How many masts does a sailboat known as a "sloop" have?

5. True or false? A full moon is twice as bright as a half moon.

6. His most famous sculpture is called *The Bronco Buster.*

7. The atom of what element is used in atomic clocks?

8. Who is the female co-star in Woody Allen's film *Sleeper*?

9. He is the son of Zeus and the messenger of the gods.

10. In golf, what is the name of the trophy given to the winner of the Open Championship?

PART B

----

1. In what state will you find Badlands National Park?

2. In miles, how long is the U.S./Mexico border?

3. True or false? Babe Ruth hit a home run in the first all-star game.

4. What was the first university founded in the United States?

5. What do we call a statistician that calculates life expectancy?

6. In the movie *Pulp Fiction,* all the clocks are set to what time?

7. What was the theme music for the TV show *The Lone Ranger*?

8. The first time a black man was depicted on a U.S. coin was in 1940. Who was he?

9. Using a standard deck of cards, how many different straight flushes are possible?

10. In the movies, a baby girl named Bonnie Blue was born to what two famous characters?

QUIZZES

E

PART C

1. Whitney Houston had a big hit with the song "I Will Always Love You." What country singer wrote the song and originally performed it in 1974?

2. True or false? The glue on the back of an Israeli postage stamp is certified kosher.

3. In what country will you find the southernmost point on mainland Europe?

4. What was the last letter added to our alphabet?

5. Current is measured in amperes. What is the SI unit for capacitance?

6. One of TV's top-rated episodes aired on November 21, 1980. What was it?

7. In our solar system all the planets rotate counterclockwise, except for which one?

8. Coins minted at the Philadelphia Mint bear what mint mark?

9. What actress, who has starred with Robert Redford and Richard Gere, did the voice of E.T. in *E.T.: The Extra-Terrestrial?*

10. Name the five major peaks in the Presidential Range of the Green Mountains that are named after U.S. presidents.

PART D

1. What world leader once said, "There is no point in taking special precautions when those who want to kill me are as incompetent as those who are supposed to protect me"?

2. Who is Freddie Prinze, Jr. married to?

3. Our paper money is not made of paper. Other than ink, what two things are our currency made of?

4. In 1908, the Model T Ford was first advertised in what periodical?

5. What are the utilities in the American version of Monopoly?

6. What is the modern name for the city once called Byzantium?

7. Whose ship was named *Queen Anne's Revenge*?

8. At what baseball stadium do Ferris Bueller and friends see a baseball game?

9. In what part of the body will you find the brachial artery?

10. Other than Jeff Lynne, name the four members of The Traveling Wilburys.

PART E

---

1. George Washington's wife was named Martha; name the only other president whose wife was named Martha.

2. R.L. Stine wrote what series of horror books for children?

3. Name the three U.S. Virgin Islands.

4. When Billy Batson said, "Shazam," what super hero did he become?

5. What comedian said, "I never forget a face, but in your case I will make an exception"?

6. Name the six most common letters used in the English language.

7. What four colors (or shades) denote the premium squares in Scrabble?

8. By what name are the fertile but treeless plains of Argentina known?

9. What actor made one of his last screen appearances as the commander of the Death Star in the movie *Star Wars*?

10. What was the name of the U.S. nickel that immediately preceded the Indian Head nickel?

QUIZ

thirteen

PART A

1. What is the capital of Maine?

2. Who coined the term *nerd*?

3. True or false? You will find the word *ginormous* in *Webster's Dictionary*.

4. What did soccer player David Beckham and his wife name their first child?

5. What singer-songwriter wrote the lyric, "You don't need a weatherman to know which way the wind blows"?

6. What famous individual said, "My cigar is not a symbol, it is only a cigar"?

7. In what year did England return control of Hong Kong to the Chinese?

8. What is the name of the Roman moon goddess?

9. What is the title equivalent to a knighthood that is conferred on a woman?

10. How many flavors did the Baskin-Robbins ice cream shop begin with back in 1948?

PART B

----

1. Eagle Scout is the highest Boy Scout rank. What is the rank below Eagle Scout?

2. Name any weight in professional boxing that falls in the welterweight class.

3. What was the first name of Col. Sherman Potter's wife on the TV show *M*A*S*H*?

4. God didn't let Moses enter the Promised Land, but he did let him see it from what mountain?

5. All the holes at Augusta National Golf Club, home of the Masters Tournament, are named after what?

6. What is the currency of Iraq?

7. According to Greek mythology, what did Oedipus do to his body when he found out that he had married his mother?

8. What professional golfer won 11 tournaments in a row?

9. What did Al Capone die of?

10. Cary Grant starred in four Alfred Hitchcock films; name them.

PART C

1. In 1998, what novel did the Modern Library list as the best novel written in English in the twentieth century?

2. What TV hero was portrayed by Clayton Moore?

3. The first line in what famous work is, "All this happened, more or less"?

4. How many strings does a cello have?

5. In what country will you find the highest volcano in Europe?

6. Who wears the polka-dotted jersey in the Tour de France?

7. Which Canadian province borders the most U.S. states?

8. How many astronauts have walked on the moon?

9. In the movie *Batman Forever,* Jim Carrey poses this riddle: "We're five little items of an everyday sort, you'll find us all in a tennis court." What is the answer?

10. Vilnius is the capital of what country?

PART D

1. Once a fad, what was the name of those hand held electronic "pets" that required so much care?

2. What was the name of the first English-born child in the Americas?

3. The nation of Lesotho is entirely surrounded by what African nation?

4. If you are in the United Kingdom and you order "gammon," what kind of food will you get?

5. Who holds the congressional record for years served in office?

6. What was the name of the, next book in the series after *The Hitchhiker's Guide to the Galaxy*?

7. What was the time interval between the dropping of the Hiroshima bomb and the Nagasaki bomb?

8. On what TV show do some men belong to an organization called "The National Organization of Men Against Amazonian Masterhood"?

9. In astronomy, what is a sysygy?

10. Without considering ties, what is the winning score that must be achieved in badminton?

PART E

1. *Canine* is the animal adjective for dogs. What is the adjective for cows?

2. What is the name of the deadly virus that Thandie Newton's character is infected with in the movie *Mission Impossible II*?

3. When this broke up, it separated into Laurasia and Gondwanaland.

4. How many time zones are in China?

5. What was the name of the man-eating plant in *The Little Shop of Horrors*?

6. In the game of pool, which two balls are red?

7. What grain or fruit is the Greek drink ouzo made from?

8. What is the medical term for baldness?

9. How many black keys are on a piano?

10. In what Woody Allen film did he utter the line, "My brain, that's my second favorite organ"?

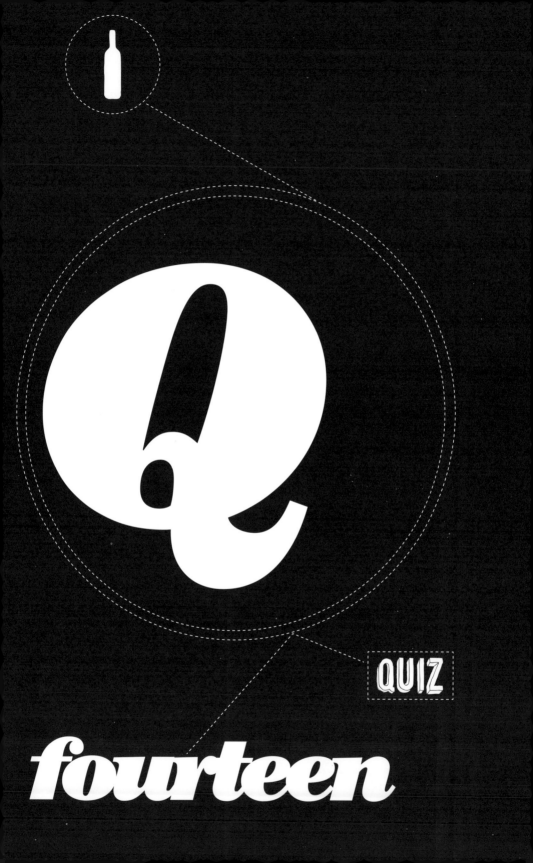

QUIZ

fourteen

PART A

1. Name the four Latin American countries that have their capital cities named after them.

2. Who is the main character in *Around the World in 80 Days*?

3. From what TV series theme song will you find the words, "Making your way in the world today takes everything you've got?"

4. True or false? Other than humans, there are no other mammals that live to be one hundred years old.

5. What was Princess Diana's maiden name?

6. In 1969, the Beatles released their last album. What was the title?

7. As evidenced by the label, which beer bills itself as "the one and only"?

8. Who is credited with inventing the machine gun?

9. In the *Star Wars* movies, who kills Quigon?

10. In terms of elevation, what capital city is the highest in the world?

PART B

----

1. Who was responsible for the discovery of vulcanized rubber?

2. Give or take five, how many children did Brigham Young have?

3. How many bones are in the human wrist?

4. In the Woody Allen movie *Sleeper*, what is the name of the sex replacing machine?

5. Yes or no: Does the average house cat have any teeth that are canines?

6. What percentage of gold is there in 14 karat gold?

7. According to pay grades, a private first class in the U.S. Army is equivalent to what rank in the U.S. Marines?

8. *The Flintstones* was based on the main characters of what 1960s sitcom?

9. In the original Hippocratic Oath, to whom did the doctor swear to uphold the standards of the profession?

10. What country singer had a huge hit with a song written for Patsy Cline called "Blue"?

PART C

1. What was the name of the terrorist group in the movie *True Lies*?

2. What 1960s group performed the hit song "He's So Fine"?

3. Tommy Tutone had a hit about a girl named Jenny; what was her phone number?

4. What was the character name of the good witch in *The Wizard of Oz*?

5. What is the minimum distance to either right or left field in Major League Baseball?

6. How many points must a stag elk have on each antler to be considered mature?

7. In what decade of the twentieth century did Picasso die?

8. Haiti and the Dominican Republic share what island?

9. What do the initials of the magazine *GQ* stand for?

10. What condition would you have if you have three copies of chromosome 21?

PART D

----

1. What well-known American once said, "I can't say that I was ever lost, but I was bewildered for three days"?

2. Name the five ABC color commentators on *Monday Night Football* that were pro quarterbacks.

3. Assuming a day on earth is exactly 24 hours, how much longer is a day on Mars?

4. To what country do the Galapagos Islands belong?

5. In the movie *My Fair Lady*, Eliza Doolittle repeats what phrase while trying to learn to speak proper English?

6. Who introduced tobacco into England in the early 1600s?

7. John Cazale starred as Fredo alongside Al Pacino in the *Godfather* movies. In what other film did they act together?

8. What breed of dog was President Richard Nixon's dog, Checkers?

9. What was the name of the command module on the *Apollo 11* mission?

10. David Leisure is best known for his lying TV commercial character named what?

PART E

1. According to the closing credits, what did John Belushi's character Bluto grow up to become in the movie *National Lampoon's Animal House*?

2. By what nickname is the Federal Home Loan Mortgage Corporation known?

3. What country uses the baht as their currency?

4. In the movie *Back to the Future*, what brand of underwear does Michael J. Fox's character wear?

5. Not including water, what was the most popular nonalcoholic drink in colonial times?

6. Truth or False? When the crew of *Apollo 11* returned to earth, they had to fill out a customs declaration.

7. In the movie *Back to School*, what dive does Rodney Dangerfield's character perform to win the diving meet?

8. Whose slogan is "We never sleep"?

9. What is the wrinkled flesh that hangs from the neck of a turkey called?

10. What is the only Central American country that uses English as its official language?

PART A

1. What is the capital of Lebanon?

2. What was the topic of the 1966 movie *Endless Summer*?

3. The American Film Institute named this character the top villain of all time.

4. In the movie *Sideways*, what type of wine does Paul Giamatti's character dislike?

5. What university's basketball team did shock jock Don Imus hurl inappropriate comments at?

6. What is the junction between adjacent nerve cells called?

7. What is the three-word catch phrase of TV network TNT?

8. What is the Italian word for bartender?

9. It's London's version of Time's Square and it is the famous intersection that is home to the Criterion Theatre, the London Pavilion, and a statue that is sometimes known as "The Angel of Christian Charity."

10. Of all the games played on a court, in which one does the ball travel the fastest?

PART B

1. What comedian was David Letterman's first guest back in 1982?

2. How many ounces of beer are in a standard keg?

3. Who are the three principals that make up the SKG in the company DreamWorks SKG?

4. All three of the books in the *Lord of the Rings* trilogy were published in what decade?

5. In the movie *Gross Pointe Blank*, what event does John Cusack's character try to avoid?

6. In geometry, what is the term used to describe an angle between 90 and 180 degrees?

7. Who was the first U.S. president to be president of all fifty states?

8. What two countries border Ecuador?

9. What was the name of the virus that infected the town of Cedar Creek in the Dustin Hoffman film *Outbreak*?

10. On the TV show *Cash Cab*, what are the two help lines that you are allowed to use?

PART C

1. What was the name of the cab company in the TV show *Taxi*?

2. On *Seinfeld*, Kramer said that if he had a child he would name it after this geometric term.

3. The state-run newspaper of the Soviet Union was called *Pravda*. What does "pravda" translate into English as?

4. The Greek alphabet begins alpha, beta, gamma, delta, and epsilon; what comes next?

5. Known for "acting," among other things, his real name is James George Janos.

6. Name the four Alfred Hitchcock films that star Jimmy Stewart.

7. Who composed the "Blue Danube" waltz?

8. What was the name of the first man-made satellite sent into orbit?

9. What was the number of Sherlock Holmes' residence on Baker Street?

10. In the movies, actors Clint Eastwood, Lee Van Cleef, and Eli Walach were known collectively as what?

PART D

1. By what name are units of force called in the SI system?

2. Yes or no: Is it possible for a woman to have just one X chromosome?

3. Who started his life out as a "King" and later became president of the United States?

4. In the computer world, what is it called when you run the system board at a higher speed than that recommended by the manufacturer?

5. What is the pen name of author Daniel Handler, who wrote 13 children's books about the unlucky Baudelaire orphans?

6. What rule change in 1937 significantly sped up the game of basketball?

7. What do Jane Seymour, Catherine Howard, and Ann Boleyn all have in common?

8. What comedian's catchphrase was "I'm a bad boy?"

9. What was the name of the news program where Murphy Brown worked?

10. What is the medical term for pink eye?

PART E

- -

1. Plus or minus five, how many counties in Louisiana were declared federal disaster areas after Hurricane Katrina?

2. What event did Tom Sawyer and Huck Finn interrupt when they returned after running away to become pirates?

3. In the movie *Kill Bill: Vol. 2*, by what means does Uma Thurman's character actually kill Bill?

4. What famous righter of wrongs rides a horse named Tornado?

5. What was the nationality of the first astronaut in space that wasn't either an American or a Russian?

6. In croquet, what are the wooden balls hit through?

7. How many gold stars are on the flag of the European Union (as of January 2009)?

8. "The man in black fled across the desert, and the gunslinger followed" is the opening line to what series?

9. What is the term used to describe a person that shoes horses?

10. Who is known for writing the line "Good fences make good neighbors?"

QUIZ

sixteen

PART A

1. What actor starred in the movies *It Could Happen To You* and *Valley Girl*?

2. In the American version of Monopoly, one of the railroads is called the B & O. What do the letters in B & O stand for?

3. Which Shakespeare play was being performed when the Globe Theatre burned down in 1613?

4. Which Mediterranean island is farthest north: Sardinia, Sicily, Malta, or Corsica?

5. According to the New York City Visitors & Convention Bureau, what is New York City's biggest parade?

6. What actress starred in the movies *Ace Ventura: Pet Detective* and *No Way Out*?

7. What well-known city was the original capital city of California?

8. How does the character Sara Connor die in the *Terminator* movies?

9. Name the two prisons at which Johnny Cash recorded albums.

10. In what country did the original person buried in Arlington, Virginia's "tomb of the unknown soldier" die?

PART B

1. What is the capital of Illinois?

2. What character in the Bible made the golden calf for the Israelites to worship?

3. Who created the fictional detective Nero Wolfe?

4. What is Wonder Woman's secret identity?

5. Which is the famous landmark Devils Tower made of: volcanic rock, sandstone, limestone, or granite?

6. Lake Champlain lies between what two states?

7. Who directed *The Maltese Falcon*, *The Man Who Would Be King*, and *Prizzi's Honor*?

8. What does the literary term *ibid* mean?

9. In the U.S. Congress, which party member enforces attendance and discipline?

10. What was the name of the boat on the TV show *Gilligan's Island*?

PART C

1. What country's capital city means, "I see the mountain"?

2. What word is used to describe the seasonal loss of hair, fur, or feathers in mammals and birds?

3. True or false? The summer is hotter because the earth is closer to the sun.

4. What name is given to the eating utensil that looks like a spoon but also has tines like a fork?

5. What candy bar was named after its inventor's family horse?

6. Which ocean or sea is the largest in terms of area: Arctic, Caribbean, or Mediterranean?

7. What nickname was given to the 1960s Western films produced by Italian studios?

8. How many players are on the ice for a penalty shot in NHL hockey?

9. What cells in the body are responsible for clumping together to form a temporary plug at the site of wounds?

10. What do the letters in VHS stand for?

★ PART D

1. What well-known pop singer's name can be spelled from the anagram I GET NEW FANS?

2. Which one of the original 13 colonies was the last to be founded?

3. Within 10 percent, when Howard Hughes sold his 75 percent stake in TWA in 1966, how much was the bank draft (check) that he received?

4. Four U.S. presidents have been assassinated. Has a British prime minister ever been assassinated?

5. Retinol is better known as what vitamin?

6. In the game of pool, or billiards, what name is given to the shot where the cue ball is caused to curve?

7. What singer's song "My Life" was the theme song for the TV show *Bosom Buddies*?

8. Who created the fictional character Natty Bumpo?

9. What test was given for the first time to athletes in the 1968 Olympics?

10. What well-known entertainer's real name is Steveland Judgkins Morris?

PART E

1. According to the words of Jesus Christ, what is the root of all evil?

2. What is the maximum speed (the only speed) of a San Francisco cable car when it is attached to the cable?

3. A worm can be traditionally found at the bottom of what beverage?

4. How many blackbirds were baked into the pie in the English nursery rhyme "Sing a Song of Sixpence"?

5. Is kohlrabi a religious leader, a medieval weapon, a vegetable, or a type of dwelling?

6. Who wrote the poetic line, "How do I love thee..."?

7. Which is farthest south: the Mexican state of Jalisco, Tabasco, or Chihuahua?

8. What caused the walls of Jericho to fall down?

9. What Alfred Hitchcock film features a dramatic scene on Mount Rushmore?

10. What is the name of the famous French impressionist who painted *The Judgment of Paris* and *The Women with Hats*?

QUIZ

seventeen

PART A

1. What is the capital of Finland?

2. What is the name for the fear of heights?

3. What do the letters in "scuba" stand for?

4. Where in Texas is the Alamo?

5. What is the title of the poem that begins with the line, "Once upon a midnight dreary, while I pondered, weak and weary?"

6. In Great Britain, if you are standing in front of a lorry, what are you in front of?

7. Thanksgiving is the day when Americans consume the most food per person. What is the second biggest day of food consumption?

8. Who is credited with discovering Florida?

9. What do the initials ALF stand for in the TV sitcom of the same name?

10. Who wrote the book *The Call of the Wild?*

PART B

----

1. What four words have appeared on all U.S. coins?

2. What female singer had a 1999 hit with the song "That Don't Impress Me Much?"

3. Which astrologic sign falls between Sagittarius and Aquarius?

4. In chess, is the white king placed on a white or black square to begin?

5. What rare bird name is also used to describe a double eagle in golf?

6. Which U.S. president said, "The only thing that we have to fear is fear itself"?

7. Vitamin B3 is also known as what?

8. The actual title of what painting is *The Arrangement in Grey and Black*?

9. Which cartoon character was the first to be blown up as a parade balloon?

10. Name the seven Sean Connery James Bond films.

PART C

----

1. What flower has more varieties than any other—more than thirty thousand?

2. What is the smallest country in the world?

3. The balance beam in gymnastics is four inches wide. Within one foot, how long is it?

4. Which narrow stretch of water separates North Africa from Spain?

5. Which U.S. president was the first to shake Fidel Castro's hand?

6. Athlete Roger Bannister was the first man to do this back in 1954.

7. What two metals are alloyed to create bronze?

8. What is the character name of the hunchbacked butler in *The Rocky Horror Picture Show*?

9. The Hundred Acre Wood is the fictional home of what main character?

10. Which Oscar winner was Al Gore's roommate at Harvard?

PART D

---

1. Where on a human would you find the spot equivalent to the fetlock on a horse?

2. Name the three ingredients in Tabasco sauce.

3. The burning point of paper provided the title for what sci-fi novel?

4. What country does Red Bull, the energy drink, originate from?

5. What ship, which launched in 1934, was the first British vessel more than 1,000 feet long?

6. What flavor is the liqueur Frangelico?

7. Where did Noah's ark come to rest?

8. In what category did Winston Churchill win a 1953 Nobel Prize?

9. What is the largest moon in our solar system?

10. What California landmark was originally built to promote a real estate venture?

PART E

1. What is the process called when a solid changes to a vapor without first becoming a liquid?

2. What is the largest island in the Mediterranean?

3. True or false? Adolf Hitler was once named *Time* magazine's "Man of the Year."

4. In mathematics, how much is a googol?

5. Humans have seven vertebrae in their necks. How many do giraffes have?

6. We get the phrase "Mind your Ps and Qs" from the British. What are the "Ps" and "Qs?"

7. What is the name of the 1950s theme restaurant in the movie *Pulp Fiction*?

8. What state is nicknamed the Beehive State?

9. More monuments have been built in honor of this individual than any other.

10. In what country is the westernmost point in continental Europe?

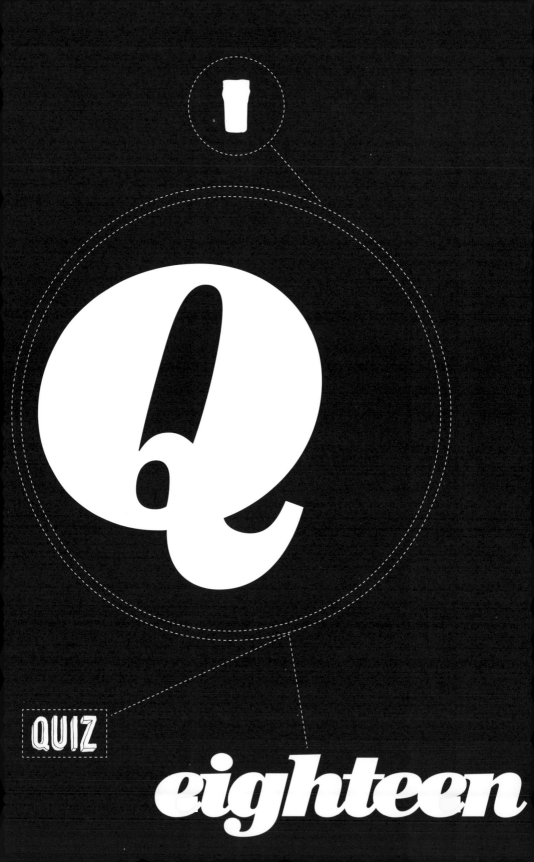

QUIZ

eighteen

PART A

1. What is the capital of Argentina?

2. According to the King James version of the Bible, how many days did Jonah spend in the belly of the great fish?

3. How many strings are on a standard guitar?

4. Who was Manfred von Richthofen?

5. In the movie *Ferris Bueller's Day Off*, what two songs does Ferris sing while on the float?

6. What is the term for a line that originates outside of a circle and touches it at only one point?

7. Jerry Springer was the mayor of what city?

8. True or false? Steven Spielberg is credited as author of the book *Close Encounters of the Third Kind*.

9. What is Dr. Evil's cat's name in the *Austin Powers* movies?

10. Who was the Republican Party's first president?

PART B

1. Bubonic plague struck Europe in the 1300s, 1400s, or 1500s?

2. Mount McKinley is the highest point in what state?

3. What kind of fish are the skipjack and bonito?

4. The last time that this occurred was in 1975 at the Manchu Red Restaurant in Detroit, Michigan.

5. Where is this line, "Gentlemen, you can't fight in here, this is the war room," from?

6. What well-known liquor is also known as "Old Number 7"?

7. What are the names of the title characters in Alexandre Dumas' *The Three Musketeers*?

8. What were the two cities in Dickens' *A Tale of Two Cities*?

9. Captain A. Roy Brown, a Canadian, is credited with killing what well-known World War I figure?

10. What is the name of the hot, oppressive wind that blows from Libya into southern Europe?

PART C

1. What animal is a domesticated breed of a wild polecat?

2. Which rock and soul singer's real name is Annie Mae Bullock?

3. From what Shakespeare play comes the line, "All the world's a stage, and all the men and women merely players"?

4. Which one of the Great Lakes is entirely within the United States?

5. What was the name of the U.S. atomic submarine that was first to circumnavigate the globe under water?

6. What is the alphabet system that uses flags called?

7. In which type of Japanese drama do men play all the parts?

8. Phillip Michael Thomas played a detective on what TV series?

9. How many men were members of the "Fellowship of the Ring"?

10. Name the seven deadly sins.

PART D

1. What type of flavor does the vegetable fennel have?

2. What two states are separated by the Mason-Dixon Line?

3. What is the name of the process of training a horse to carry out a set routine of movements in competition?

4. How tall are the letters in the famous Hollywood sign?

5. The Sahara of Africa is the largest desert; where will you find the second largest?

6. What was Mark Twain's real name?

7. Who said, "The coldest winter I ever spent was a summer in San Francisco"?

8. During the Civil War, in what state would you have found the southernmost point among the states that remained loyal to the union?

9. True or false? Willie Nelson once smoked pot on the roof of the White House.

10. What is the name of the competition where teams of male golfers from the United States compete against Europeans?

QUIZZES

----

1. What well-known edifice is located near the city of Agra?

2. How did Sharon Tate die?

3. Which European country's capital city is the most northerly?

4. What was the name of the playwright that married Marilyn Monroe?

5. In what year did Cal Ripken's consecutive game streak begin?

6. What is the pair of glands located at the upper aspect of the kidneys called?

7. In Steinbeck's *The Grapes of Wrath*, the family moved from what state to what state?

8. What country did Israel principally fight in the Six-Day War?

9. What was Michelangelo's first name?

10. Which body of water separates Poland from Sweden?

QUIZ

nineteen

PART A

1. What is the capital of Illinois?

2. In what city is the Pro Football Hall of Fame?

3. What kind of food is the Italian dish called a frittata?

4. What is the ticker symbol for Anheuser Busch?

5. What nationality was Alfred Nobel?

6. Who built their empire first: the Mayas or the Incas?

7. In the movie *Castaway*, what was Tom Hanks' kickable sidekick's name?

8. Who said, "Give me liberty or give me death"?

9. Unlike most major newspapers, what will you not find on the front page of the *Wall Street Journal*?

10. How many tentacles does a squid have?

PART B

----

1. Does the photon have a positive, a negative, or no charge?

2. What two countries are separated by the Pyrenees Mountains?

3. In what decade was bubblegum invented?

4. Mélange is the name of the hallucinogenic spice in what book?

5. What actor starred in *Raising Arizona*, *Moonstruck,* and *Honeymoon in Vegas*?

6. Mark David Chapman is infamous for killing whom?

7. While in the Galapagos, Charles Darwin studied 14 species of what bird?

8. The largest standard size is a Churchill, but it only measures about seven inches. What is it?

9. True or false? The area code that includes Cape Canaveral is 3-2-1.

10. What is the medical term for uncontrollable sudden attacks of sleep?

$\mathcal{B}$ $\mathcal{B}\mathcal{B}\mathcal{B}$ B

PART C

1. Famous for the first flight, in what state is Kitty Hawk located?

2. Which Indian led the attack on Custer at the Battle of Little Big Horn?

3. What was director Tim Burton's first major motion picture directorial debut?

4. Who played the elusive blond in the Thunderbird in the movie *American Graffiti?*

5. Who was the first sports great to have his number retired by his team?

6. What poet is the author of "Paul Revere's Ride"?

7. What is the English translation of the word *kamikaze?*

8. What is the highest point in California?

9. Tess Trueheart is the wife of what comic strip character?

10. What animal appears on the reverse of the Canadian one dollar coin first minted in 1988?

PART D

- -

1. The Declaration of Independence begins with what three words?

2. A crocodile can move faster on land or in water?

3. What is the longest river in Ireland?

4. What was Lucy Ricardo's maiden name on *I Love Lucy*?

5. What gangster was the FBI's first "public enemy number one"?

6. If you travel directly east from New York City, what non-island country will you reach first?

7. The part of your body known as the axilla is better known as what?

8. What is the largest state east of the Mississippi?

9. Hank Aaron hit his 715th home run against what team?

10. Eugene Cernan was the last person to do this in 1972.

PART E

----

1. What was Juliet's age at the beginning of *Romeo and Juliet*?

2. What is the best card total in the game of baccarat?

3. Your bank deposits are insured by the FDIC; what do the letters stand for?

4. In the movie *The Princess Bride,* what poison does Vizzini try to give Wesley?

5. Pro golfing legend Gary Player hails from what country?

6. The Borg Warner trophy is awarded to the winner of what?

7. What actor played "Mr. Pink" in the movie *Reservoir Dogs*?

8. What is the name of Grant Wood's famous painting of a farm couple with a man holding a pitch fork?

9. How long does it take light from the sun to reach the earth?

10. After Eric Clapton left the Yardbirds, what famous lead guitarist took his place?

QUIZ

twenty

PART A

1. What is the capital of North Carolina?

2. From what county do we get Red Stripe beer?

3. Which was discovered first: penicillin or the polio vaccine?

4. What prefix in the metric system signifies a billionth part?

5. According to the King James version of the Bible, what number commandment is "Though shall not commit adultery"?

6. Which of these islands is one of the Lesser Antilles: Jamaica, Cuba, Barbados, or Puerto Rico?

7. In Morse code, what is the sequence for SOS?

8. What is the nickname for the Indianapolis 500 speedway?

9. Which president sent Lewis and Clark on their famous expedition?

10. What would someone from Britain call the hood of their car?

PART B

1. What are the names of the two long bones of your forearm?

2. What is the Egyptian symbol of life called?

3. How long is the Channel Tunnel (Chunnel)?

4. Which constitutional amendment provides for a speedy trial?

5. What state borders Kansas to the north?

6. Based on their life spans, could Confucius have met the Buddha?

7. What football player portrayed the character Mongo in the movie *Blazing Saddles*?

8. Yes or no: Do Uruguay and Paraguay share a border with each other?

9. What does the constellation of Orion represent?

10. What do the letters in UNICEF stand for?

PART C

----

1. What movie star's name can be derived from the anagram OLD WEST ACTION?

2. What is an ecdysiast?

3. Not counting 1999, name any year that the Susan B. Anthony dollar was minted.

4. Walt Whitman wrote the poem "When Lilacs Last in the Dooryard Blooms" about whose funeral?

5. What two bodies of water are connected by the Suez Canal?

6. What is the derivative of 3X squared plus 7?

7. The flag of the Philippines is red and blue. Is it red on top, blue on top, or sometimes red and sometimes blue?

8. Which word in this sentence is the penultimate one?

9. What is the name of the track where the Kentucky Derby is held?

10. Name the five states that the Continental Divide crosses.

PART D

----

1. What do we call the city of Peking now?

2. On sheet music, what do the bar lines separate?

3. He composed "The Way We Were" and "Nobody Does it Better."

4. How many spots on a pair of dice?

5. What is the southernmost U.S. state?

6. What two sports make up the Olympic biathlon?

7. Who said, "Religion is the opiate of the masses"?

8. Wilt Chamberlain scored one hundred points in a single NBA game against what team?

9. According to Greek mythology, who stole fire and gave it to man?

10. What river does the United States Military Academy at West Point lie on?

PART E

1. How old was Maria Sharapova when she won the 2006 U.S. Open?

2. The Dr. Seuss classic *Green Eggs and Ham* contains 1–50, 51–100, or 101–150 *different* words?

3. What was the name of the country club in the movie *Caddyshack*?

4. Which one of the following is an inert gas: oxygen, radon, hydrogen, or nitrogen?

5. What post-impressionist painter is known for his works entitled *The Tahitians* and *Spirit of the Dead Watching*?

6. Which two people were not mentioned in the theme music of *Gilligan's Island* during the first season?

7. Including Alaska and Hawaii, in what state will you find the geographic center of the United States?

8. According to the Terman's classification, above what number is considered a genius IQ?

9. How many locks are there in the Panama Canal?

10. The president's plane is known as Air Force One. What is the president's helicopter known as?

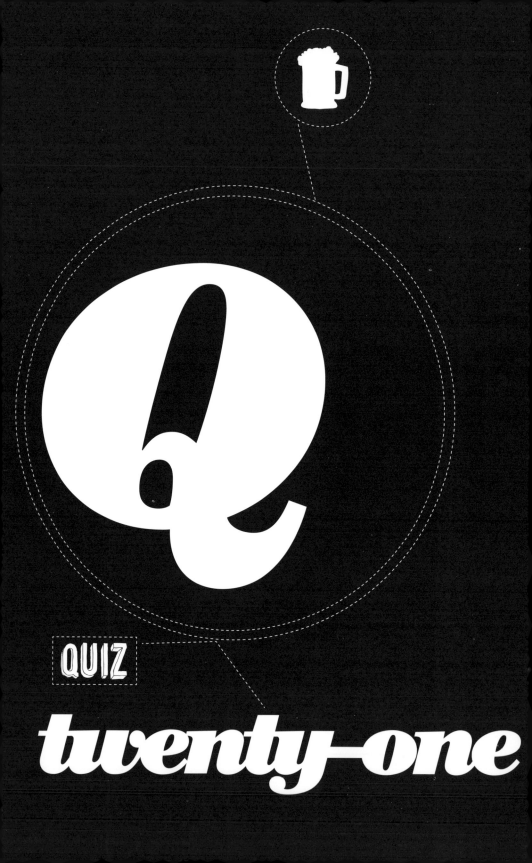

PART A

----

1. Do the people of Kentucky pronounce the name of their state capital as: Looieville, Louis-ville, Loo-ville, or another way?

2. Who was it that terrorized an area known as White Chapel?

3. Which is closer to the earth, Venus or Mars?

4. Prior to 1939, by what name was Thailand known?

5. From what Beatles song is the lyric, "The girl with kaleidoscope eyes"?

6. In the movie *Wayne's World*, Wayne and Garth greet what rock star by saying, "We're not worthy"?

7. From what country do we get Goldschläger cinnamon schnapps?

8. What are you afraid of if you are ergophobic?

9. What sports figure said, "You observe a lot just by watching"?

10. Which is farthest from New York City: The Sea of Cortez, the Red Sea, or the Sea of Tranquility?

PART B

1. What is the name of the actor that plays Mini-Me in the *Austin Powers* movies?

2. What is the formula for the area of a triangle?

3. In what city will you find Tulane University?

4. Who wrote a symphony known as *Water Music*?

5. What well-known singer had a big hit with the song "Soak Up the Sun"?

6. Who, back in 1983, made the longest run from scrimmage—99 yards?

7. In the sport of cutting, what are you trying to cut away?

8. In what state were Bonnie and Clyde ambushed by Texas Rangers?

9. Which continent is the closest land mass to Antarctica?

10. How many constellations are officially recognized by the astronomical congress?

PART C

- -

1. Who invented the revolver in 1835?

2. In degrees Kelvin, what is absolute zero?

3. What is the average temperature on earth? (2009)

4. Players from what team were charged with conspiring to throw the 1919 World Series?

5. *La Giaconda* is the actual title of what famous work?

6. What organization coined the phrase, "Do not fold, spindle, or mutilate?"

7. Who is actor Marion Michael Morrison better known as?

8. What river flows through Vienna, Belgrade, and Budapest?

9. Which NHL team has won the most Stanley Cups?

10. Which is farthest west: Reno, Nevada or Los Angeles, California?

QUIZZES

PART D

----

1. What is the name of the small fleshy mass that hangs at the back of your mouth?

2. A male donkey is called an ass; what is a female called?

3. Who is the author of *Gulliver's Travels*?

4. In an American classic movie, what were characters Joel Cairo and Kaspar Gutman looking for?

5. Who was on the U.S. quarter immediately before George Washington?

6. What comic strip artist was the first to win a Pulitzer Prize?

7. Before they were called the Hawaiian Islands, what did we call them?

8. According to the song, Yogi Bear is smarter than what?

9. Who was the only actor to star in *The Magnificent Seven* and *The Dirty Dozen*?

10. Using pay grades, a major in the U.S. Army is equivalent to what rank in the U.S. Navy?

PART E

1. How old was Ronald Reagan when he took his second oath of office?

2. Whose autobiography was entitled *Where's the Rest of Me?*

3. Which came first: Scrabble or Monopoly?

4. In what famous structure will you find the Hall of Mirrors?

5. The two youngest men inducted into the baseball hall of fame were both 36 when they received this honor. Who were they?

6. Osiris was the Egyptian god of what?

7. Who shot Robert F. Kennedy?

8. What is the fastest animal on two legs?

9. Within 10 degrees, what is the minimum tilt necessary for a bowling pin to fall over?

10. Yes or no: Do peacocks lay eggs?

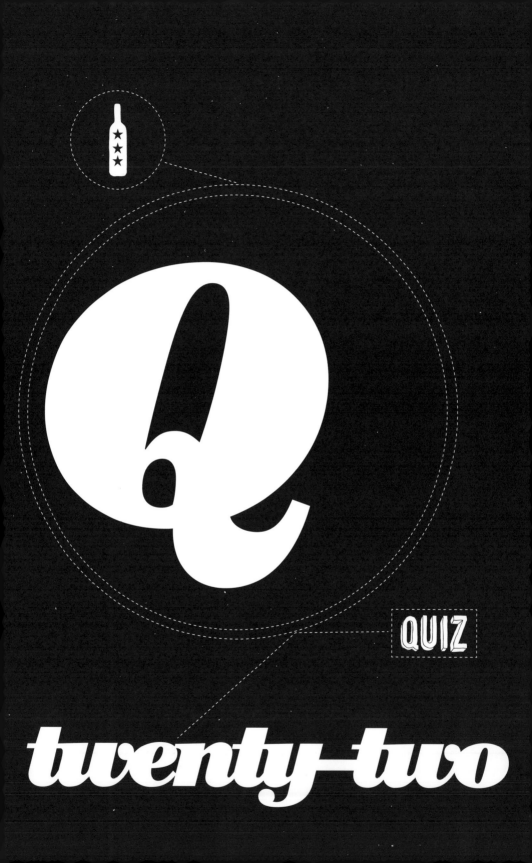

QUIZ

twenty-two

PART A

1. What are the names of the two gangs in *Westside Story?*

2. Filberts are a food more commonly known by what name?

3. Name any year that Genghis Khan was alive.

4. In the *Star Wars* universe, on what planet do the Ewoks live?

5. How many states border Mexico?

6. What famous performer died from an unexpected punch to the stomach?

7. What does it mean if a satellite is at its apogee?

8. What was on the back of the Lincoln penny prior to the monument?

9. What flag is known as the Stars and Bars?

10. What is the nickname of the lowest man in the graduating class of the United States Naval Academy in Annapolis?

PART B

----

1. Who is the only American man in the last 75 years to win the marathon in the Olympics?

2. How many letters does a player draw to begin the game of Scrabble?

3. What is the chemical symbol for plutonium?

4. Which artist became famous from his posters of Parisian entertainers and prostitutes?

5. Name the three states that don't participate in daylight savings time.

6. Only one southern capital east of the Mississippi was not captured by the Union in the U.S. Civil War; which one?

7. What state is bordered by both Carolinas?

8. What does the term *brut* mean when applied to champagne?

9. Who is the voice of Bart Simpson?

10. What word is used to describe a word that sounds like the thing it refers to?

PART C

1. In the English language, more words begin with this letter than any other.

2. What are the impulses traveling on the olfactory nerve associated with?

3. How long was Sleeping Beauty asleep?

4. Other than being called Italians, people that live in Naples, Italy, are called what?

5. In what year will Haley's comet return?

6. In Greek mythology, where is the home of the gods?

7. What gospel says, "Blessed are the meek for they shall inherit the earth"?

8. The movie *Goodfellas* was based on the real life of what criminal?

9. What is the only U.S. state capital that has three words?

10. True or false? You can find the term *McJob* in the dictionary, where it is defined as a low-paying job.

PART D

----

1. What is the capital of Delaware?

2. If you are eating a type of sushi called *unagi*, what are you eating?

3. Gettysburg is in what state?

4. Elzie Crisler Segar created this well-known comic strip that spawned cartoons and movies.

5. What event in the 1980s took sixty lives and destroyed more than 150 square miles in the United States?

6. What is a palindrome?

7. Which of the Great Lakes is the westernmost?

8. The Motel Six chain opened in 1962. What was the original room rate?

9. Water is H_2O; what is H_2O_2?

10. Which Confederate state was the first to rejoin the Union after the Civil War?

PART E

1. In what state will you find Princeton University?

2. Who are the Friends of Bill W.?

3. What is the name of the single large continent that was present on earth 250 million years ago?

4. What was the nickname of the gateway between East and West Berlin?

5. On a golf course, what kind of marker is specifically used to identify out of bounds?

6. On a movie set, what is a gaffer?

7. At what temperature does Fahrenheit equal Celsius?

8. What ocean separates Russia and Greenland?

9. What is the most likely place that you would hear the instrumental march entitled "Entry of the Gladiators"?

10. What term describes when dissimilar organisms live together in a mutually beneficial relationship?

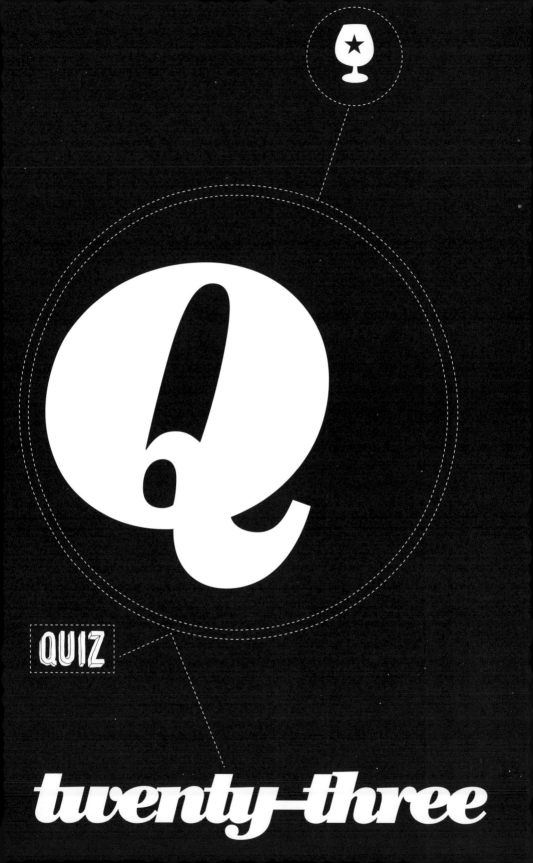

QUIZ

twenty-three

PART A

1. Quito is the capital of what country?

2. *Semper fi* is short for a Latin phrase meaning what in English?

3. What is the collective name given to a group of lions?

4. In what film did Roger Moore debut as 007?

5. The three main greenhouse gases are chlorofluorocarbons and what two others?

6. What is the bell in the clock tower in the Houses of Parliament in London called?

7. In what sport might you find a bucket, a washout, and a sleeper?

8. Which Wright brother flew the first flight?

9. The Scoville scale measures the heat of peppers. Plus or minus 25, what is the value of a green pepper?

10. What are you suffering from if you have circadian dysrhythmia?

PART B

1. What do the letters in the space term EVA (spacewalk) stand for?

2. Yes or no: Did Lewis and Clark ever reach the Pacific Ocean?

3. What character pulled the curtain back and revealed that the Wizard of Oz was a fake?

4. In what city will you find the running of the bulls each July?

5. Which of these animals is the slowest: zebra, giraffe, or grizzly bear?

6. What shape is the Milky Way galaxy?

7. What was the name of the protective underclothing worn by Frodo in *The Lord of the Rings?*

8. In English the title of whose book is translated as *My Struggle?*

9. What kind of energy is possessed by a stretched spring?

10. What author in 1729 suggested the modest proposal that the Irish eat their young?

PART C

1. What is a close encounter of the second kind?

2. Mount Vesuvius is located nearest which one of the following: Naples, Milan, Florence, or Rome?

3. In what Irish city did Bloody Sunday occur?

4. Who invented calculus?

5. What designer produces the perfume called Opium?

6. Tony Clifton was the alter ego of what famous comedian?

7. Which U.S. president was the first to throw out the opening pitch for a season in Major League Baseball?

8. In *Sleepless in Seattle*, what city did Meg Ryan's character come from?

9. Only at the Olympics in Albertville were the athletes awarded medals that were made from something other than gold, silver, and bronze; what were they made of?

10. What is the actual technical name for the funny bone?

PART D

----

1. Country singer Keith Urban is married to what actress?

2. How many number one songs did Elvis have on the U.S. pop charts?

3. In craps, what did you roll if you roll a "little Joe"?

4. He said, "The meek shall inherit the earth, but not the mineral rights."

5. The author of the book *Chitty Chitty Bang Bang* is best known for creating what literary character?

6. Name the northernmost and southernmost national capitals.

7. The football game in what military movie is decided by a play in which the center is eligible?

8. Who composed the *1812 Overture*?

9. What eight states border Tennessee?

10. What substance do you create by heating sodium hydroxide and fat?

PART E

1. Who wrote the novel *Ulysses*, heralded by Modern Library as the number one book on its list of best novels written in English in the twentieth century?

2. "Oye Como Va" was popularized by Carlos Santana but written by "the King of Latin Music." Who was he?

3. What is necessary for a golf course to be called properly a links course?

4. Name the four main islands of Japan.

5. Only one vice president of the United States has ever become president without succeeding the president that he served. Who is he?

6. On TV's *Star Trek: The Next Generation,* what beverage does Captain Piccard always order?

7. The ancient Egyptians venerated lots of living things; they also worshipped a God named Sebek. What kind of animal was Sebek?

8. After Disneyland opened in 1955, how many weeks did it take before they reached their one millionth visitor?

9. Which gas has the characteristic smell of rotten eggs?

10. In the original 1964 *Pink Panther* movie, who, or what, was the pink panther?

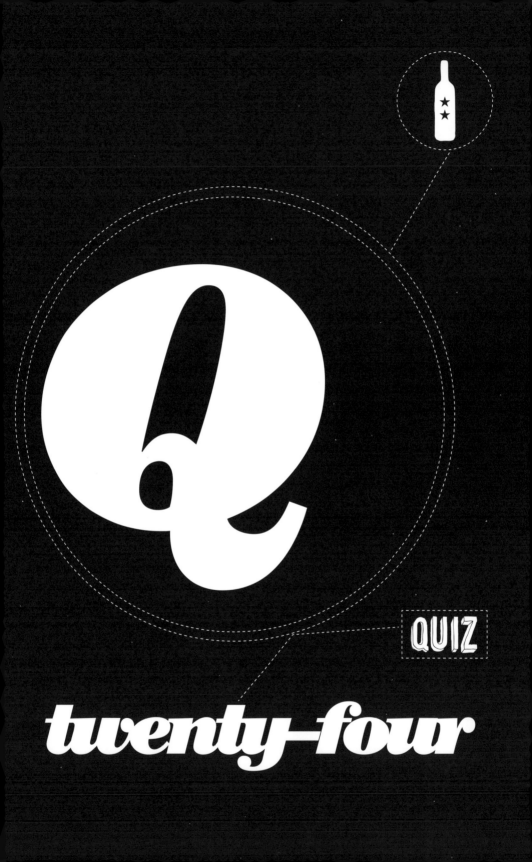

QUIZ

twenty-four

PART A

1. Which island is the capital of New Zealand located on: north or south?

2. Which director said, "The length of a film should be directly related to the endurance of the human bladder"?

3. Is the pistil the male or the female part of the flower?

4. Which side of the *Titanic* hit the iceberg: starboard or portside?

5. How much does the Roman numeral *L* stand for?

6. In the NHL, how long do you spend in the penalty box for a minor infraction of the rules?

7. What were the names of the king and queen that sponsored Columbus' voyage to the new world?

8. What famous London street is known for men's tailoring?

9. According to the King James version of the Bible, how many people were aboard Noah's ark?

10. What is the name for Mexican tripe soup?

PART B

1. Who did Tony Blair defeat to become prime minister in 1997?

2. What color are 98 percent of all airline flight recorder boxes painted?

3. What is the chemical symbol for arsenic?

4. What body of water separates South Korea from China?

5. According to the movie *Pulp Fiction*, a Quarter Pounder is called a Royale with cheese in France. Before France adopted the Euro, if you walked into a McDonald's with 100 francs, could you buy a Royale with cheese?

6. Which tennis player said, "Sex doesn't affect your tennis, it's staying out all night trying to find it that affects your game"?

7. How many times each day do Muslims pray?

8. From what city are the places named on the original Monopoly board?

9. California, Alaska, and Texas are the three largest states by area. What are the next two largest?

10. What is the nickname of the notorious killer David Berkowitz?

PART C

1. How many stars are on the California state flag?

2. What did Howard Carter discover in 1922?

3. What is the average time between eruptions of the Old Faithful geyser?

4. What country is the world's leading coffee producer?

5. What is the three letter ticker symbol for the auction house Sotheby's?

6. Who discovered that white light can be separated into the colors of the rainbow?

7. Starting in 1976, who won five consecutive Wimbledon men's singles championships?

8. If you dig straight through the earth from the center of the United States, you won't come out in China. In fact, you'll hit water. Where will you come out?

9. Who is writer Eric Blair better known as?

10. What two large cities are at each end of Route 66?

PART D

1. What is the name of the coffee shop that Frasier and Niles frequent in the sitcom *Frasier*?

2. What is the fastest growing land-based plant?

3. Who was it that hit the golf shot on the moon?

4. What was Zimbabwe called before it changed its name in 1980?

5. Born July 25, 1978, what is Louise Brown famous for?

6. "Suicide Is Painless" is the theme music to what TV show?

7. On many early flags in the United States, you might find the words "Don't tread on me" alongside a picture of what?

8. What do the letters in Disney's "EPCOT" theme park stand for?

9. What does the Fujita scale measure?

10. In what U.S. state will you find the highest waterfall?

PART E

1. What year did prohibition end in the United States?

2. The coasts of what two countries form the Bay of Biscay?

3. Name any year that Rembrandt was alive.

4. What is the order, as you look at it from left to right, of the presidents on Mount Rushmore?

5. What does a nanometer measure?

6. Who composed "The Flight of the Bumblebee"?

7. What was the nickname of the serial killer in the movie *Silence of the Lambs*?

8. From which Shakespearean work do we get the phrase, "Neither a borrower nor a lender be?"

9. If you perform a *mea culpa,* what have you done?

10. What kind of animal was the first animal sent into space?

PART A

1. What is the capital of Oregon?

2. What is the name of the machine that maintains the ice at a professional hockey game?

3. Minnesota is known as "The Land of 10,000 Lakes," but in actuality, are there officially more or less than 10,000 lakes?

4. What is the most visited home in the United States?

5. What is the highest number on a dart board?

6. In 1988, Mike Tyson earned $20 million for knocking out what fighter in just 91 seconds?

7. Who is older: Paul McCartney or Mick Jagger?

8. What is the pH of the strongest base?

9. Who wrote *Dr. Jekyll and Mr. Hyde*?

10. What well-known figure is nicknamed the "Iron Lady"?

PART B

1. True or false? Residents of Alaska get a check just for living there.

2. Who said, "Nothing is certain but death and taxes"?

3. How many times did Mohammed Ali successfully defend his world heavyweight championship?

4. What does the first 20 in the 20/20 vision measurement stand for?

5. What is sodium bicarbonate better known as?

6. In what movie did Clint Eastwood say, "Go ahead, make my day"?

7. What article of clothing would you remove to expose your malleolus?

8. Who is Goldie Hawn's famous daughter?

9. What is the name of the effect responsible for an ambulance siren having a higher pitch as it approaches?

10. Two of this singer's four kids are named Ahmet and Diva Muffin. What are the names of the two better-known kids?

PART C

1. Which U.S. state is immediately south of Montreal, Canada?

2. What is the technique used by novice snow skiers to slow down or stop (not falling down)?

3. What is the name of the character or the actress who has the longest run on the TV show *Law and Order*?

4. What layer of the earth is between the crust and the core?

5. Name the tall, flightless, running Australian bird.

6. Other than eggs, what is the defining ingredient in eggs Florentine?

7. Who was the first foreign-born player to win golf's Masters Tournament?

8. Name the only state that Ronald Reagan did not win in the 1984 U.S. presidential election?

9. Who was the longest reigning British king in history?

10. Although not born yet, this character will be born in Riverside, Iowa, on March 21, 2228.

PART D

1. What actress married John McEnroe in 1986?

2. In economics, what do the letters GNP stand for?

3. Plus or minus ten, in what year did the Washington Monument open to the public?

4. After the Japanese attacked Pearl Harbor, where was the Declaration of Independence moved to?

5. Which Greek mathematician noted that the shortest distance between two points is a straight line?

6. In what unique way do clowns register their "faces"?

7. In Indian cooking you find the term *tandoori*; what does *tandoor* mean?

8. In the movie *Trading Places*, what did the Duke Brothers try to corner the market in?

9. On a cellular level, what is the process of sexual reproduction called?

10. What is the name of the official groundhog of Groundhog Day?

PART E

1. What state capital is the southernmost of the 48 continental states?

2. In London, what industry is most associated with Fleet Street?

3. Which actress starred in *The War of the Roses* and *Romancing the Stone*?

4. From what country do we get the cha-cha?

5. What name was given to the relocation of the Indian tribes to land beyond the Mississippi River?

6. If both teams are at full strength, how many players are on the ice in a professional hockey game?

7. What is a Foley artist?

8. Tippi Hedren is famous for her role in Hitchcock's film *The Birds*. Who is her famous daughter?

9. From what movie do we get the line, "What we have here is failure to communicate"?

10. As written in English, all Japanese words end either in a vowel or what letter?

ANSWERS

Quiz 1

PART A

1. Rome
2. October
3. Smoking
4. Yes
5. Roundabout
6. Bases
7. Dowsing
8. "Live Strong"
9. Ten
10. Counting Crows, *Shrek 2*

PART B

1. Penguins
2. 15,000
3. Woody Allen
4. Johnny Rivers
5. Thomas Edison
6. President of Mexico
7. *Twelfth Night*
8. El Capitan in Yosemite, California
9. Melbourne
10. Babe

PART C

1. Liverpool
2. . 111
3. Alabama
4. Georgia O'Keefe
5. *The MythBusters*
6. The Silver State
7. Lunar Excursion Module
8. Fifteen
9. Yes, in 1952
10. *Roger & Me, The Big One, Bowling for Columbine, Fahrenheit 911, Sicko,* and *Capitalism: A Love Story*

PART D

1. Lime and salt
2. Key West
3. Eight
4. 1966 Thunderbird
5. Jalisco
6. He complained about guilt over masturbation.
7. Toronto Blue Jays
8. Miu Miu
9. Astronaut
10. !, @, #, $, %, ^ , &

PART E

1. Coors
2. Sausage and Yorkshire pudding (the batter)
3. *Field of Dreams, Bull Durham,* and *For the Love of the Game*
4. 23.5 degrees
5. Who's there?
6. Busta Rhymes and P. Diddy
7. Paraguay
8. Emily Brontë
9. Earth pig
10. Idle hands

Quiz 2

PART A

1. *Kramer vs. Kramer*
2. Isis
3. Catalysts
4. A cappella
5. Alighieri
6. Ivory soap
7. F
8. 75 percent
9. Jane Russell
10. A wardrobe

PART B

1. Sarasota
2. 159°F
3. Primates
4. Diane Chambers
5. 64 percent
6. Salt
7. Eurocents
8. Noxzema
9. 9-9-9
10. Dorothy Lamour

PART C

1. Sea of Japan or East Sea
2. Oregon (Portland)
3. A Ferrari
4. Largest asteroids in the solar system
5. Pete Townsend
6. Parrotheads
7. They were red, white, and blue
8. Cheeta
9. John Wilkes Booth; Brutus said it first.
10. June 14th

PART D

1. The death of James Dean
2. Four: Illinois, Michigan, Ohio, and Kentucky
3. Hindenburg disaster
4. Martin Scorsese
5. Mel Gibson
6. The Red Queen
7. H.J. Heinz
8. Limestone
9. Jane Pauley
10. Denali National Park

PART E

1. The Dallas Cowboys Cheerleaders
2. Martin Van Buren
3. 25 times
4. Dubble Bubble Bubble Gum
5. Land of the pilgrims' pride
6. Bob Seger and "Night Moves"
7. The Heisenberg Uncertainty Principle
8. Fastest Finger competition
9. A triangle
10. Fiji

Quiz 3

PART A

1. Bishop
2. Mrs. O'Leary's
3. 24
4. Bolivia and Argentina
5. *Blade Runner*
6. South Pole
7. Brent Spinner, Data of *Star Trek* fame
8. F117
9. 4,187 miles long
10. Chalk

PART B

1. 1871
2. Banana cream
3. Himself
4. Very superior old pale
5. Ferrari
6. Wing and finger; a dinosaur
7. Louis the XVI
8. Aaron
9. Pale yellow
10. A string

PART C

1. Mayonnaise
2. Italy and Austria
3. *Mary Poppins*
4. Amsterdam
5. Skynet
6. Britain and China
7. Blue square
8. Incus, Malleus, and Stapes
9. Parker and Barrow
10. Four months

PART D

1. Seattle Grace
2. John Williams
3. Salem
4. The Black Sea
5. Henry Derringer
6. U.S. Treasury
7. *Chicago*
8. John F. Kennedy
9. Cat makeup
10. Germany

PART E

1. Four
2. Budapest
3. New Mexico
4. 14th
5. The nose
6. John Steinbeck
7. Australia
8. 1988
9. Jones
10. Spain, France, U.S. Republic of Texas, Confederate, and Mexico

Quiz 4

PART A

1. Bern
2. June or July
3. Arkansas
4. A billionth of a second
5. Boyle's law
6. 92.5 percent
7. Lewd acts with actor Hugh Grant
8. King George III
9. He was an IRS agent.
10. Surfing

PART B

1. Ben Franklin
2. 1914
3. Armadillo
4. Acetic acid
5. Ecuador
6. 42
7. *The Life of Brian*
8. Reserve Officers Training Corp.
9. Elvis Presley
10. Bock's Car

PART C

1. A kiss
2. Ursula Andres
3. Roger Maris
4. Athena
5. Joanne Kathleen
6. Talc
7. *Carmen*
8. Yes
9. 1950s
10. Ireland

PART D

1. Stimpmeter
2. John F. Kennedy
3. Tree nymph
4. Loch Ness
5. The Shadow
6. Cubism
7. Joe Lewis
8. Willow
9. Climb Mount Niitaka
10. 102

PART E

1. Her first born child
2. North and South Islands of New Zealand
3. 1969
4. Everything
5. Jerry, the animated cartoon mouse
6. Swan
7. The Crickets
8. John le Carré
9. *The Music Man*
10. A bicycle

Quiz 5

PART A

1. Panama City
2. An egg
3. Vodka, Kahlúa, and Bailey's Irish Cream
4. Jigsaw puzzle
5. By a crocodile
6. Daniel Craig
7. Yes
8. HBO
9. Methane
10. There's no change.

PART B

1. *East of Eden*
2. The Gideons International
3. Planet
4. Japan
5. The Washington quarter
6. A king
7. Nocturne
8. A golden fiddle
9. Sue Grafton, The Alphabet Murders
10. Indonesia

PART C

1. A perfect number
2. White Castle
3. Spleen
4. The Phoenix
5. France
6. 220 yards
7. Stonehenge
8. Before the Common Era
9. True
10. Vatican City, San Marino, Lichtenstein, Luxembourg, Monaco, and Andorra

PART D

1. Tahiti
2. Protozoa
3. Anakin Skywalker
4. Swahili
5. George
6. Gerald Ford
7. Nine
8. False
9. Zero, they don't store water in their humps
10. Quebec

PART E

1. It has no tail.
2. Pamela Anderson
3. Saber
4. Cardinal
5. The Great Pumpkin
6. 1972
7. *Hamlet*
8. 6th floor
9. *Titanic*
10. Callisto, Titan, Ganymede, and Io

Quiz 6

PART A

1. Kuala Lumpur
2. Computer Generated Imaging
3. Variety
4. Coca-Cola
5. *Flatliners*
6. The watery part of milk
7. Sugar
8. True
9. 16
10. John Phillips Sousa

PART B

1. Uruguay
2. 1924
3. D. H. Lawrence
4. Insulin
5. 1940s
6. Grover Cleveland
7. Ghana
8. Basic Input and Output System
9. Nixon and Kennedy
10. Zero

PART C

1. "You've Lost that Lovin' Feeling" by the Righteous Brothers
2. Phillip K. Dick
3. Virginia
4. Foreigners
5. Gwyneth Paltrow
6. *The Daily Planet*
7. Igor Stravinsky
8. Be right back
9. Nome and Anchorage
10. New Mexico, Arizona, and Oklahoma

PART D

1. False
2. Pari-mutuel betting
3. Ra
4. Ethan Allen
5. Lombard Street in San Francisco
6. North and South Korea
7. Mad cow disease
8. The Boston Strangler
9. *A Hard Days Night, Help, Magical Mystery Tour, Yellow Submarine,* and *Let it Be*
10. The Goodwill Games

PART E

1. 35
2. Pelé
3. True
4. Airplane
5. Dextrose
6. *Carpathia*
7. Traci Lords
8. Truman Capote
9. Blue laws
10. San Bernardino

Quiz 7

PART A

1. Montgomery
2. She was burned at the stake.
3. The Wailers
4. Clavicle
5. Chicken
6. False
7. Rene Descartes
8. *Pulp Fiction*
9. Fifth
10. Lyndon Johnson

PART B

1. *Jeopardy*
2. Chief Justice Marshall in 1835
3. Jon Lovitz
4. Ken Norton, Joe Frazier, Leon Spinks, and Larry Holmes
5. True
6. Five-cent cigar
7. Tanzania
8. Great Dane
9. Lucille Ball
10. Au

PART C

1. Formaldehyde
2. Juan Valdez
3. John Adams
4. Athena
5. The ski jumper that falls at the beginning of ABC's *Wide World of Sports.*
6. Paul Wolfowitz
7. $100 platinum eagle
8. Ottawa
9. Isaac Asimov
10. Kentucky, Massachusetts, Pennsylvania, and Virginia

PART D

1. Car racing (also golf on the infield)
2. Monet
3. False, it is the mockingbird.
4. Cologne
5. Billie Jean King
6. 11
7. Glass
8. 31
9. Quakers
10. *E pluribus unum*

PART E

1. Aristotle
2. The Seven Sisters Colleges
3. Bob Dylan
4. Eyes
5. Ireland
6. Raisins
7. Washington Irving
8. *Alice in Wonderland*
9. Inert or noble gases
10. Betty Grable

Quiz 8

PART A

1. Bogotá
2. True
3. Stomach
4. Pavlov
5. The Hague, Netherlands
6. Three
7. Green
8. The Sphinx
9. Michael Jackson's
10. Honus Wagner, Ty Cobb, and Babe Ruth

PART B

1. Milky Way bar
2. 440 yards
3. Massachusetts
4. General MacArthur
5. England
6. 2,000 miles
7. Liberia (capital is Monrovia)
8. Caspian Sea
9. Faber College
10. New Jersey

PART C

1. John Lennon
2. Zero
3. Morgan Freeman
4. Mountaineering
5. Sweetened condensed milk
6. Small intestine
7. Czechoslovakia
8. American female to go to space
9. Estée Lauder
10. Bing Crosby

PART D

1. Snickers Almond
2. Riverdance
3. True
4. *The Lost World*
5. Coca-Cola
6. The males only
7. Richard Gere and Brad Pitt
8. Robert Fulton
9. Mississippi, Missouri, St. Lawrence, Rio Grande, and Yukon
10. Hemorrhoids

PART E

1. Shooting Israeli athletes at the Olympics
2. Maryland and Virginia
3. Ben Franklin
4. The mother of the pilot that dropped the bomb on Hiroshima
5. Phoenix
6. 8,000 miles
7. Bushmills
8. Paul McCartney
9. Coast Guard
10. Harvard, Yale, Brown, Princeton, University of Pennsylvania, Cornell, Columbia, and Dartmouth

Quiz 9

PART A

1. Bismarck
2. Emerald
3. Victory
4. True
5. Eighty
6. B
7. Penicillin
8. El Paso
9. Playing violin
10. Right field

PART B

1. *Of Mice and Men*
2. *2001: A Space Odyssey*
3. Banish pain and sorrow
4. California
5. Vivian Leigh
6. Systolic and diastolic
7. Bruce Willis and Cybill Shepherd
8. Women Auxiliary Service Pilots
9. Lyndon Johnson
10. Cuba

PART C

1. St. Louis, Los Angeles, and Atlanta
2. Nine
3. The bicycle business
4. Ann-Margret
5. Woodrow Wilson
6. "My Sweet Lord"
7. James Callahan
8. 1.5 liters
9. Tin, copper, and zinc
10. James Joyce

PART D

1. Pieces of the rind
2. Franking
3. The Doors ("Light My Fire")
4. True
5. India
6. Leonard Bernstein
7 Kauai
8. Rush Limbaugh
9. Nina Simone
10. Chicago

PART E

1. Las Vegas
2. 9.81 meters-per-second squared
3. Czech Republic
4. Pennsylvania
5. Chang and Eng
6. Arizona
7. Sydney
8. Denmark
9. Coccyx
10. Theo

Quiz 10

PART A

1. Sri Lanka
2. Veal
3. Edith Head
4. Vegetable
5. None, it is only for three-year-olds
6. Kodak
7. True
8. On his head
9. Binion's
10. Lincoln in his Gettysburg Address

PART B

1. Brazil
2. James Polk
3. Pulmonary
4. Carnivore
5. Sagittarius
6. Marc Antony
7. 1970
8. Smack
9. Hanson
10. Alliteration

PART C

1. Greenland
2. Patchouli oil
3. Calliope
4. Don Diego
5. Boston
6. The mobile
7. Glass
8. *Sleeping with the Enemy*
9. Kentucky Fried Chicken
10. The Monterey Bay Aquarium

PART D

1. Ramada
2. The Three Stooges
3. John Milton
4. Anthony Hopkins
5. Old Fashioned
6. e (natural logarithm)
7. Laughing gas
8. The Netherlands
9. The alkaline earth metals
10. Boxing

PART E

1. Imclone
2. Mossad
3. *Annie Get Your Gun*
4. River Phoenix
5. Clark Gable
6. Gout
7. Davis Cup
8. Mediterranean Sea
9. Gazpacho
10. Determining the age of trees by their rings

Quiz 11

PART A

1. Morocco
2. The diaphragm and the intercostals
3. David Bowie
4. Ursula
5. Saturn
6. No
7. Bavarian Motor Works
8. Beefalo
9. 1906
10. A wolf

PART B

1. Belgium
2. Rocky and Bullwinkle
3. 2,150 miles
4. The passenger seat
5. The escudo
6. Have a drink
7. 100 inches per year
8. Italy and Sicily
9. Magna Carta
10. Apache

PART C

1. Seppuku
2. Rome
3. Mickey Rooney
4. Hudson Bay
5. Twelve
6. Stretching
7. Paprika
8. Acetylsalicylic acid
9. John Lennon and Yoko Ono
10. Adenine, cytosine, guanine, and thymine

PART D

1. Mersey
2. Jugular
3. Sir Francis Drake
4. Georgia
5. Plums
6. Taiwan
7. Herman Göring
8. Trillion or trillant
9. Mah-jongg
10. Swimming, cross country, fencing, riding, and shooting

PART E

1. Zion
2. "Satisfaction"
3. Taxonomy
4. Martin Van Buren
5. 2.5 miles
6. The Sex Pistols
7. One
8. Atlantic City
9. Agamemnon
10. Grape-Nuts (It's made by Post.)

Quiz 12

PART A

1. Madison
2. Lay them straight
3. Four
4. One
5. False, it's nine times brighter
6. Frederick Remington
7. Cesium
8. Diane Keaton
9. Hermes
10. Claret jug

PART B

1. South Dakota
2. 1,951 miles
3. True
4. Harvard
5. An actuary
6. 4:20
7. "William Tell Overture"
8. Booker T. Washington
9. Forty
10. Scarlett O'Hara and Rhett Butler

PART C

1. Dolly Parton
2. True
3. Spain
4. J
5. Farad
6. The episode of *Dallas* when we learned who shot JR
7. Venus
8. None
9. Debra Winger
10. Lincoln Mountain, Mount Grant, Mount Cleveland, Mount Roosevelt, and Mount Wilson

PART D

1. Charles de Gaulle
2. Sarah Michelle Gellar
3. Cotton and linen
4. *Saturday Evening Post*
5. Electric Co. and Waterworks
6. Istanbul
7. Blackbeard's
8. Wrigley Field
9. Arm
10. George Harrison, Bob Dylan, Roy Orbison, and Tom Petty

PART E

1. Thomas Jefferson
2. *Goosebumps*
3. Saint Croix, Saint Thomas, and Saint John
4. Captain Marvel
5. Groucho Marx
6. R, S, T, L, N, and E
7. Pink, light blue, dark blue, and red
8. Pampas
9. Peter Cushing
10. Liberty Head nickel

Quiz 13

PART A

1. Augusta
2. Dr. Seuss
3. True
4. Brooklyn
5. Bob Dylan
6. Sigmund Freud
7. 1997
8. Diana or Luna
9. Dame
10. 31

PART B

1. Life Scout
2. 140–147 pounds
3. Mildred
4. Mount Nebo
5. Trees, flowers, or shrubs
6. Dinar
7. Blinded himself
8. Byron Nelson
9. Syphilis
10. *Suspicion, Notorious, To Catch a Thief*, and *North by Northwest*

PART C

1. *Ulysses*
2. The Lone Ranger
3. *Slaughterhouse Five*
4. Four
5. Italy, Mount Aetna
6. The best hill climber
7. Ontario
8. 12
9. Vowels
10. Lithuania

PART D

1. Tamagotchi
2. Virginia Dare
3. South Africa
4. Ham
5. Strom Thurmond
6. *The Restaurant at the End of the Universe*
7. Three days
8. NO MA'AM was featured on the show *Married with Children*
9. When all the planets align
10. 15

PART E

1. Bovine
2. Chimera virus
3. Pangaea
4. One
5. Audrey 2
6. 3 and 11
7. Grapes
8. Alopecia
9. 36
10. *Sleeper*

Quiz 14

PART A

1. Brazil, Panama, Guatemala, and Mexico
2. Phileas Fogg
3. *Cheers*
4. True
5. Spencer
6. *Abbey Road*
7. Newcastle
8. Gatling
9. Darth Maul
10. La Paz, Bolivia

PART B

1. Charles Goodyear
2. 57
3. Eight
4. The orgasmatron
5. Yes, four
6. 58 percent or 7/12
7. Lance corporal
8. *The Honeymooners*
9. Apollo
10. Leann Rimes

PART C

1. Crimson Jihad
2. The Chiffons
3. 867-5309
4. Glinda
5. 325 feet
6. Six
7. 1973
8. Hispaniola
9. *Gentleman's Quarterly*
10. Down's Syndrome

PART D

1. Daniel Boone
2. Don Meredith, Fran Tarkenton, Joe Namath, Dan Fouts, and Boomer Esiason
3. 37 minutes
4. Ecuador
5. "The rain in Spain stays mainly in the plain."
6. Sir Walter Raleigh
7. *Dog Day Afternoon*
8. Cocker spaniel
9. Columbia
10. Joe Isuzu

PART E

1. Senator
2. Freddie Mac
3. Thailand
4. Calvin Klein
5. Chocolate
6. True
7. The Triple Lindy
8. The Pinkerton Agency
9. Wattle
10. Belize

Quiz 15

PART A

1. Beirut
2. Surfing
3. Hannibal Lecter
4. Merlot
5. Rutgers
6. Synapse
7. We Know Drama
8. Barista
9. Piccadilly Circus
10. Jai Lai

PART B

1. Bill Murray
2. 15 gallons or 1,920 ounces
3. Steven Spielberg, Jeffrey Katzenberg, and David Geffen
4. 1950s
5. Ten-year reunion
6. Obtuse
7. Dwight D. Eisenhower
8. Columbia and Peru
9. Motaba virus
10. Shout outs: street and mobile

PART C

1. The Sunshine Taxi Company
2. Isosceles
3. The Truth
4. Zeta
5. Jesse Ventura
6. *Rope, Vertigo, Rear Window,* and *The Man Who Knew Too Much*
7. Johann Strauss
8. *Sputnik 1*
9. 221B
10. *The Good, The Bad, and the Ugly*

PART D

1. Newtons
2. Yes, it's called Turner's syndrome.
3. Gerald Ford changed his name from Leslie King.
4. Overclocking
5. Lemony Snicket
6. The removal of the jump ball after each basket scored
7. They were all wives of Henry VIII.
8. Lou Costello
9. *FYI*
10. Conjunctivitis

PART E

1. Zero, there are no counties, only parishes
2. Their own funeral
3. The five-point palm exploding heart technique
4. Zorro
5. Czech
6. Wickets
7. 12
8. Stephen King's *Dark Tower* Series
9. Ferrier
10. Robert Frost

Quiz 16

PART A

1. Nicolas Cage
2. Baltimore and Ohio
3. *Henry VIII*
4. Corsica
5. St. Patrick's Day
6. Sean Young
7. San Jose
8. She dies from leukemia.
9. San Quentin and Folsom Prison
10. France during World War II

PART B

1. Springfield
2. Aaron
3. Rex Stout
4. Diana Prince
5. Volcanic rock
6. New York and Vermont
7. John Huston
8. In the same place
9. Whip
10. SS *Minnow*

PART C

1. Montevideo, Uruguay
2. Molting
3. False
4. Spork
5. Snickers
6. Arctic, they are listed in order by size.
7. Spaghetti Westerns
8. Two
9. Platelets
10. Video Home System

PART D

1. Gwen Stefani
2. Georgia
3. $546,549,171 (acceptable range for answer: $491,000,000–$601,000,000)
4. Yes, Spencer Perceval
5. Vitamin A
6. Masse
7. Billy Joel
8. James Fennimore Cooper
9. Genetics test for sex
10. Stevie Wonder

PART E

1. The love of money
2. 9 mph
3. Mescal (not tequila)
4. 24
5. Vegetable
6. Elizabeth Barrett Browning
7. Tabasco
8. Noise: horns and shouting
9. *North by Northwest*
10. Pierre August Renoir

Quiz 17

PART A

1. Helsinki
2. Acrophobia
3. Self-contained underwater breathing apparatus
4. San Antonio
5. "The Raven"
6. A truck
7. Super Bowl Sunday
8. Ponce de Leon
9. Alien life form
10. Jack London

PART B

1. United States of America (it's not In God We Trust)
2. Shania Twain
3. Capricorn
4. Black
5. Albatross
6. F.D.R.
7. Niacin
8. *Whistler's Mother*
9. Felix the Cat
10. *Dr. No, From Russia with Love, Goldfinger, Thunderball, You Only Live Twice, Diamonds Are Forever,* and *Never Say Never Again*

PART C

1. Orchids
2. Vatican City
3. 16 feet, 3 inches
4. Strait of Gibraltar
5. President Clinton
6. Run an under-4-minute mile
7. Copper and tin
8. Riff Raff
9. Winnie the Pooh
10. Tommy Lee Jones

PART D

1. Calf
2. Vinegar, salt, and red pepper
3. *Fahrenheit 451*
4. Austria
5. *Queen Mary*
6. Hazelnut
7. The mountains of Ararat
8. Literature
9. Ganymede
10. The Hollywood sign

PART E

1. Sublimation
2. Sicily
3. True, in 1938
4. The number 1 followed by 100 zeros
5. Seven
6. Pints and quarts
7. Jack Rabbit Slims
8. Utah
9. Buddha
10. Portugal

Quiz 18

PART A

1. Buenos Aires
2. Three days
3. Six strings
4. The Red Baron
5. *Danke Schoen* and *Twist and Shout*
6. Tangent
7. Cincinnati
8. True
9. Mr. Bigglesworth
10. Abraham Lincoln

PART B

1. 1300s
2. Alaska
3. Tuna
4. The last time Jimmy Hoffa was seen
5. *Dr. Strangelove or: How I Learned to Stop Worrying and Love the Bomb*
6. Jack Daniels
7. Porthos, Athos, and Aramis
8. London and Paris
9. The Red Baron
10. Sirocco

PART C

1. Ferret
2. Tina Turner
3. *As You Like It*
4. Lake Michigan
5. *Triton*
6. Semaphore
7. Kabuki
8. *Miami Vice*
9. Two
10. Pride, envy, gluttony, lust, anger, greed, and sloth

PART D

1. Licorice
2. Pennsylvania and Maryland
3. Dressage
4. 45 feet
5. Australia
6. Samuel Clemens
7. Mark Twain
8. California
9. True, during the Carter administration
10. Ryder Cup

PART E

1. Taj Mahal
2. She was murdered by the Manson family.
3. Helsinki
4. Arthur Miller
5. 1982
6. Adrenals
7. Oklahoma to California
8. Egypt
9. Michelangelo is his first name
10. Baltic Sea

Quiz 19

PART A

1. Springfield
2. Canton, Ohio
3. An Italian omelet
4. BUD
5. Swedish
6. Mayas
7. Wilson
8. Patrick Henry
9. Photographs
10. Ten

PART B

1. No charge
2. Spain and France
3. 1920s (1928)
4. *Dune*
5. Nicholas Cage
6. John Lennon
7. Finches
8. Cigar
9. True
10. Narcolepsy

PART C

1. North Carolina
2. Crazy Horse
3. *Pee Wee's Big Adventure*
4. Suzanne Somers
5. Lou Gehrig
6. Henry Wadsworth Longfellow
7. Divine wind
8. Mount Whitney
9. Dick Tracy
10. Loon

PART D

1. "When in the (course of human events…)"
2. On land
3. Shannon River
4. McGillicuddy
5. John Dillinger
6. Portugal
7. Armpit
8. Georgia
9. Dodgers
10. Walk on the moon

PART E

1. 13
2. Nine
3. Federal Deposit Insurance Corporation
4. Iocaine Powder
5. South Africa
6. Indianapolis 500
7. Steve Buscemi
8. *American Gothic*
9. Eight minutes
10. Jimmy Page

Quiz 20

PART A

1. Raleigh
2. Jamaica
3. Penicillin
4. Nano
5. The seventh
6. Barbados
7. Three dots, three dashes, three dots
8. The Brickyard
9. Thomas Jefferson
10. Bonnet

PART B

1. Radius and ulna
2. Ankh
3. 31 miles
4. Sixth
5. Nebraska
6. Yes
7. Alex Karas
8. No
9. A hunter
10. United Nations International Children's Emergency Fund

PART C

1. Clint Eastwood
2. A stripper
3. 1979–1981
4. Abraham Lincoln
5. The Mediterranean and the Red Seas
6. 6X
7. Red on top when at war, blue on top when at peace
8. Penultimate
9. Churchill Downs
10. New Mexico, Colorado, Wyoming, Idaho, and Montana

PART D

1. Beijing
2. Measures
3. Marvin Hamlisch
4. 42
5. Hawaii
6. Skiing and rifle shooting
7. Karl Marx
8. New York Knicks
9. Prometheus
10. Hudson River

PART E

1. 19
2. 50 exactly
3. Bushwood
4. Radon
5. Paul Gauguin
6. The Professor and Maryann
7. South Dakota
8. 140
9. Six
10. Marine One

Quiz 21

PART A

1. D. They pronounce it Frankfort.
2. Jack the Ripper
3. Venus
4. Siam
5. "Lucy in the Sky with Diamonds"
6. Alice Cooper
7. Switzerland
8. Work
9. Yogi Berra
10. Sea of Tranquility (it's on the moon)

PART B

1. Vern Troyer
2. ½ the base multiplied by the height
3. New Orleans
4. Handel
5. Sheryl Crow
6. Tony Dorsett
7. An animal from the rest of the herd
8. Louisiana
9. South America
10. 88

PART C

1. Samuel Colt
2. Zero
3. 59°F
4. Chicago White Sox
5. *Mona Lisa*
6. IBM
7. John Wayne
8. The Danube
9. Montreal Canadians
10. Reno

PART D

1. Uvula
2. Jenny
3. Jonathan Swift
4. The Maltese Falcon
5. Ben Franklin
6. Gary Trudeau
7. The Sandwich Islands
8. The average bear
9. Charles Bronson
10. Lt. Commander

PART E

1. 73
2. Ronald Reagan
3. Monopoly
4. Palace of Versailles
5. Sandy Koufax and Lou Gehrig
6. The underworld
7. Sirhan Sirhan
8. Ostrich
9. 7.5 degrees
10. No, peahens do.

Quiz 22

PART A

1. Jets and Sharks
2. Hazelnuts
3. 1162–1227 BC
4. Endor
5. Four
6. Houdini
7. It is the furthest from the Earth in its orbit.
8. Wheat
9. The Confederate flag
10. Anchorman

PART B

1. Frank Shorter
2. Seven
3. Pu
4. Toulouse-Lautrec
5. Hawaii, Arizona, and Indiana
6. Tallahassee, Florida
7. Georgia
8. Dry
9. Nancy Cartwright
10. Onomatopoeia

PART C

1. S
2. Smell
3. 100 years
4. Neapolitans
5. 2061
6. Mount Olympus
7. The Gospel of Matthew
8. Henry Hill
9. Salt Lake City
10. True

PART D

1. Dover
2. Freshwater eel
3. Pennsylvania
4. Popeye the Sailor
5. Eruption of Mount St. Helens
6. A word or phrase that is spelled the same forward and backward
7. Lake Superior
8. Six dollars
9. Hydrogen peroxide
10. Tennessee

PART E

1. New Jersey
2. Alcoholics, members of Alcoholics Anonymous
3. Pangaea
4. Checkpoint Charlie
5. White stakes
6. Chief electrician
7. -40°F
8. Arctic Ocean
9. At the circus
10. Symbiosis

Quiz 23

PART A

1. Ecuador
2. Always faithful
3. Pride
4. *Live and Let Die*
5. Carbon dioxide and methane
6. Big Ben
7. Bowling
8. Orville
9. Zero
10. Jet lag

PART B

1. Extra Vehicular Activity
2. Yes
3. Toto
4. Pamplona
5. Grizzly bear
6. Spiral
7. Mithril
8. Adolf Hitler's *Mein Kampf*
9. Potential energy
10. Jonathan Swift

PART C

1. Sighting of a UFO with evidence, such as a photo
2. Naples
3. London Derry
4. Isaac Newton
5. Yves Saint Laurent
6. Andy Kaufman
7. William Howard Taft
8. Baltimore
9. Crystal
10. Ulnar nerve

PART D

1. Nicole Kidman
2. 18
3. A pair of twos
4. J. Paul Getty
5. James Bond
6. Reykjavik and Wellington
7. *M*A*S*H*
8. Tchaikovsky
9. Arkansas, Missouri, Kentucky, Virginia, North Carolina, Georgia, Alabama, and Mississippi
10. Soap

PART E

1. James Joyce
2. Tito Puente
3. Must be near the seashore
4. Honshu, Shikoku, Hokkaido, and Kyushu
5. Richard Nixon
6. Tea, Earl Grey, hot
7. Nile crocodile
8. Seven
9. Hydrogen sulfide
10. Rare diamond

Quiz 24

PART A

1. North
2. Hitchcock
3. Female
4. Starboard
5. 50
6. Two minutes
7. Ferdinand and Isabella
8. Savile Row
9. Eight: Noah, his wife, their three sons, and their sons' wives
10. Menudo

PART B

1. John Major
2. Orange
3. As
4. Yellow Sea
5. No, the Franc is no longer legal tender.
6. Andre Agassi
7. Five
8. Atlantic City
9. Montana and New Mexico
10. Son of Sam

PART C

1. One
2. King Tut's tomb
3. 74 minutes
4. Brazil
5. BID
6. Sir Isaac Newton
7. Bjorn Borg
8. Indian Ocean
9. George Orwell
10. Chicago and Los Angeles (Santa Monica)

PART D

1. Café Nervosa
2. Bamboo
3. Alan Shepard
4. Rhodesia
5. She was the first test-tube baby.
6. *M*A*S*H*
7. Rattlesnake
8. Experimental Prototype Community of Tomorrow
9. The strength of tornados
10. California, at Yosemite

PART E

1. 1933
2. Spain and France
3. 1606–1669 BC
4. Washington, Jefferson, Roosevelt, Lincoln
5. Wind
6. Nicolai Rimsky-Korsakov
7. Buffalo Bill
8. *Hamlet*
9. You have taken the blame.
10. A dog named Laika

Quiz 25

PART A

1. Salem
2. Zamboni
3. More
4. The White House
5. 20
6. Michael Spinks
7. Paul McCartney
8. 14
9. Robert Louis Stevenson
10. Margaret Thatcher

PART B

1. True
2. Ben Franklin
3. Nine
4. Feet, the distance to the eye chart
5. Baking soda
6. *Sudden Impact*
7. Shoes or socks
8. Kate Hudson
9. Doppler Effect
10. Moon Unit and Dweezel

PART C

1. New York
2. Snow plow
3. Lt. Anita Van Buren played by S. Epatha Merkeson
4. Mantle
5. Emu
6. Spinach
7. Gary Player
8. Minnesota
9. George III
10. James T. Kirk from *Star Trek*

PART D

1. Tatum O'Neil
2. Gross National Product
3. 1888
4. Fort Knox
5. Euclid
6. They paint their faces on eggshells.
7. Clay oven
8. Orange juice
9. Meiosis
10. Punxsutawney Phil

PART E

1. Austin, Texas
2. The newspaper industry
3. Kathleen Turner
4. Cuba
5. The Trail of Tears
6. 12
7. Someone who recreates sound in synchronization to a film
8. Melanie Griffith
9. *Cool Hand Luke*
10. N

QUIZZES

Crocodiles and Alligators

1. What singer had a hit with the song "Crocodile Rock"?

2. Which U.S. president had a pet alligator that he kept in the East Room of the White House?

3. What is the nickname of the avocado that fits with this theme?

4. Which James Bond film featured a scene where Bond is trapped in an alligator farm?

5. What was the name of the 1976 film starring and directed by Burt Reynolds that fits this quiz's theme?

6. In what 1999 film do Bridget Fonda and Bill Pullman battle a big crocodile?

7. From the TV show *Miami Vice*, what was the name of the pet alligator?

8. What is the two-word common term used to express skepticism about a person's show of sympathy for the misfortune of others?

9. What tennis champion was nicknamed "Le Crocodile"?

10. In the movie *Crocodile Dundee*, in what small area in Australia was the movie set?

Literature—The Classics

Name the authors of these novels that are among the top one hundred novels written in English in the twentieth century, as voted by the board of the Modern Library.

1. *Ulysses*

2. *The Great Gatsby*

3. *Lolita*

4. *Brave New World*

5. *The Sound and the Fury*

6. *Catch-22*

7. *Slaughterhouse Five*

8. *The Wings of the Dove*

9. *As I Lay Dying*

10. *Lord of the Flies*

11. *The Sun Also Rises*

12. *The Secret Agent*

13. *The Naked and the Dead*

14. *The Maltese Falcon*

15. *Main Street*

Fifteen Degrees of Separation

For the following, simply provide the missing actor/actress or movie to complete the chain to link Mel Brooks to his late wife, the actress Anne Bancroft.

Mel Brooks starred in the movie _____

with Bill Pullman who starred in _____

with _____ who starred in _____

with Geena Davis who starred in *Thelma and Louise*

with _____ who starred in _____

with Anthony Hopkins who starred in *The Silence of the Lambs* with

_____ who starred in _____

with Mel Gibson who starred in _____

with Danny Glover who starred in *Bat 21*

with _____ who starred in *Runaway Jury*

with John Cusack who starred in _____

with Annette Bening who starred in _____

with _____ who starred in *The Negotiator*

with Samuel L. Jackson who starred in _____

with Bridget Fonda who starred in _____

with Anne Bancroft.

The Power of Three

1. Which New York Yankee wore the number 3 on his jersey between 1924 and 1934?

2. What is the name of the most famous Chinese gang that fits this quiz's theme?

3. What was the name of the third book in the *Harry Potter* series?

4. Name the three actors that had title roles in the movie *Three Men and a Baby*.

5. Name the three geographic locations that form the points of the Bermuda Triangle.

6. Six actors played parts as "The Three Stooges." The obvious three characters were Moe, Larry, and Curly. Name the other three character names.

7. Name the "Three Tenors."

8. Name the three actors that had title roles in the film *Three Amigos*.

9. Name the three Confederate men memorialized on Stone Mountain.

10. What was Newton's third law of motion?

The Bond Bonus

Name the movie associated with the following Bond gadgets.

1. Dentonite toothpaste

2. Bowler hat

3. Dagger shoes

4. Atac

5. Jet pack

6. Radioactive lint

7. Yo-yo saw

8. Spike fan

9. Solex agitator

10. Mini rocket cigarette

North American Geography

1. What is the highest point in the continental United States?

2. What is the lowest point in the continental United States?

3. In what state will you find Arches National Park?

4. What four states meet at the "Four Corners"?

5. Name the four states that border California.

6. In terms of area, which province in Canada is the largest?

7. After the Mississippi and the Missouri, what are the two next longest rivers in the United States?

8. New York City is made up of five boroughs. Name them.

9. In what state will you find Stone Mountain, where the figures of three prominent Confederate figures are carved?

10. Which one of the Great Lakes is the only one that is entirely within the United States?

Mystery Theme #1

1. According to the Ben & Jerry's Web site, what is their most popular flavor?

2. What is the name of the movie in which Woody Allen plays a character named Fielding Mellish, a man trying to impress a social activist named Nancy, who was played by Louise Lasser?

3. What is the nickname of the athletic teams at Syracuse University?

4. Brick mortar can be made by mixing water and sand with calcium oxide (CaO). CaO is better known as what?

5. What is the name of the 1929 movie in which the Marx Brothers run a hotel in Florida?

6. What is the name of the Irish band who had a hit with the 1993 song, "Dreams," which was off their *Everybody Else is Doing It, So Why Can't We?* album?

7. In the movie *Willy Wonka and the Chocolate Factory*, at what point does the gum always go wrong?

8. When considered as a separate language, what language has more native speakers than any other language?

9. Prior to the introduction of metal to fashion the heads of the golf clubs that are known as "woods," the highest quality of heads were made from what wood?

10. Complete the following line from the Steve Miller song "Jungle Love": "I met you on somebody's island; you thought you had known me before, I bought you a crate of ..."?

One-*Hit* Wonders

For the next two quizzes, use the following list of one-hit-wonders to match the artist to the song.

(Notes: You will want to make photocopies of this list for the quiz-takers.)

Nena

Dexy's Midnight Runners

Des'ree

Stacey Q

Quiet Riot

Haddaway

House of Pain

C.W. McCall

Baha Men

David Soul

The Mary Jane Girls

Thomas Dolby

Starland Vocal Band

Wild Cherry

Taco

Sugarhill Gang

Timbuk3

Los Del Rio

Nick Gilder

Crash Test Dummies

Bow Wow Wow

The Verve

4 Non Blondes

Ratt

Gerardo

Falco

Sir Mix-a-Lot

Van McCoy

Norman Greenbaum

Soft Cell

Divinyls

Spandau Ballet

Men Without Hats

Twisted Sister

Jermaine Stewart

The Waitresses

The Vapors

Vickie Sue Robinson

Deee-Lite

Bobby McFerrin

One-Hit Wonders #1

1. "Come on Eileen"

2. "Convoy"

3. "Baby Got Back"

4. "The Safety Dance"

5. "Who Let the Dogs Out?"

6. "Don't Worry, Be Happy"

7. "Rapper's Delight"

8. "Puttin' on the Ritz"

9. "Bittersweet Symphony"

10. "She Blinded Me with Science"

One-Hit Wonders #2

1. "Turning Japanese"

2. "The Macarena"

3. "Play that Funky Music"

4. "Two of Hearts"

5. "99 Luftballoons"

6. "Rico Suave"

7. "Turn the Beat Around"

8. "Spirit in the Sky"

9. "What Is Love"

10. "Hot Child in the City"

Last Lines #1

For each of the following, supply the movie from which the last line was uttered. A "helpful" hint is included.

1. "A man's got to know his limitations."
    Hint: Do you know the second one?

2. "I have to warn you, I've heard relationships based on intense experience never work."
    "Okay, we'll have to base it on sex then."
    "Whatever you say ma'am."
    Hint: If it weren't for decapitation, these two might not have gone head over heels for each other.

3. "Go! Proclaim liberty throughout all the lands, and to all the inhabitants thereof."
    Hint: Doesn't mention freedom of speech.

4. "Fat man, you shoot a great game of pool."
    "So do you, Fast Eddie."
    Hint: Sarah was played by Piper Laurie.

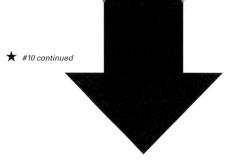
5. "What makes you so sure? Hey ... I'm back!"

   Hint: This time they didn't pay the piper.

6. "Eliza, where the devil are my slippers?"

   Hint: Wouldn't it be loverly?

7. "Where ya headed cowboy?"
   "Nowhere special."
   "Nowhere special. I always wanted
   to go there."
   "Come on."

   Hint: If you're gonna leave, take a limousine.

8. "I never had any friends later on like the
   ones I had when I was twenty-three. Jesus,
   does anyone?"

   Hint: The novel was written by Stephen King—really!

9. "Louis, I think this is the beginning of a
   beautiful friendship."

   Hint: Ask Dooley Wilson; he might do it again

10. "Well, nobody's perfect."

    Hint: Apparently "Friends of Italian Opera" aren't the
    least bit interested in sugar cane. Boy, what they are
    missing!

Mystery Theme #2

1. In the 1960s, what city was the center of the Mersey beat music scene?

2. The types of wines that are commonly described as white, ruby, and tawny are all what kind of wines?

3. Louis Armstrong had the nickname Satchmo; the "satch" part is an abbreviation for satchel. What is the "mo" short for?

4. What are the chemical symbols for tungsten and of barium?

5. What is the name of the daughter of former President Bill Clinton?

6. What is the common name of the place where weapons and ammunition are stored and issued from?

7. In 1913, what beer company adopted the blue star as its trademark?

8. What is the last name of the well-known singer that broke up with his fiancée, Nicolette Sheridan, in August 2008?

9. Is the state of Illinois north, south, east, or west of Indiana?

10. Prosciutto is the Italian word for what?

Literature— The Readers' List

Name the authors associated with these books, which were voted among the best written in English in the twentieth century by "the readers."

1. Atlas Shrugged

2. Battlefield Earth

3. To Kill a Mockingbird

4. The Moon is a Harsh Mistress

5. Gravity's Rainbow

6. Gone with the Wind

7. The Stand

8. The French Lieutenant's Woman

9. The Hitchhiker's Guide to the Galaxy

10. The World According to Garp

11. Something Wicked This Way Comes

12. The Call of the Wild

13. Watership Down

14. The Hunt for Red October

15. The Satanic Verses

Taglines #1

Name the movie to which these taglines are associated.

1. "They'll never get caught. They're on a mission from God."

2. "Does for rock 'n' roll what the *Sound of Music* did for the hills."

3. "Leisure rules, or one man's struggle to take it easy."

4. "The first casualty of war is innocence."

5. "The world is ours."

6. "Just when you thought it was safe to go back into the water."

7. "The truth is out there."

8. "Nice planet, we'll take it."

9. "The classic story about a boy and his mother."

10. "You'll laugh, you'll cry, you'll hurl."

Mystery Theme #3

----

1. In this 2002 film, Jason Statham's character has three rules: Never change the deal, no names, and never open the package. What is the film?

2. What letter is added to the end of the stock ticker symbol to indicate that the company is involved in bankruptcy proceedings?

3. Premiering in 2005, what is the name of the TV show in which each episode focuses on an FBI case concerning the mystery of human remains? The female lead is played by Emily Deschanel.

4. He is one of the most influential golf architects of our time. He designed the TPC Sawgrass, home of the Players Championship, and La Quinta in Palm Springs, to name just a few. Who is he?

5. Which chemical element has atomic number 3?

6. He is the only tennis player in the "open era" to have won Wimbledon and the French Open in the same year more than once. He did it three consecutive times, in 1978, 1979 and 1980; who is he?

7. What was the name of the band Pearl Jam's 1991 debut album?

8. In basketball, what position did Elgin Baylor and Scottie Pippin both play?

9. What kind of particles are said to come in flavors?

10. What is the name of the first plane to fly around the world without refueling?

Stars and Bars

The answers to the following questions are related to stars and bars. Please fill in the blanks, and sorry, Moe's Tavern and Cheers are not among the answers.

1. What is the name of the bar on the TV show *Three's Company*?

2. What artist painted *Starry Night*?

3. What was the name of the bar that the *Cheers* gang competed against?

4. How many stars on the flag of the People's Republic of China?

5. What flag is known as "The stars and bars?"

6. What is the name of the bar on the TV show *Buffy the Vampire Slayer*?

7. Complete the following Blondie lyric (six words): "'Cause the man from Mars stopped eatin' cars and eatin' bars and now...."

8. What is the name of the bar on the TV show *M*A*S*H*?

9. What is the name of the bar where John Travolta and Debra Winger hung out in the movie *Urban Cowboy*?

10. How many stars does a major general in the U.S. Army wear?

Pop Tarts and Breakfast Snacks

----

1. Kellogg's Pop-Tarts come two to a foil package. How many calories are in two Brown Sugar Cinnamon Pop-Tarts, give or take fifty calories?

2. True or false? Kevin Bacon is a vegetarian.

3. Name the manufacturer for each of the following breakfast cereals (Note: give one half point for each correct answer).

   A. Apple Jacks
   B. Cap'n Crunch
   C. Cocoa Pebbles
   D. Trix
   E. Wheaties

4. Who am I?

I was born in 1890 and lived until 1941. I was an American virtuoso pianist, bandleader, and composer who some call the first true composer of jazz music. My business card referred to me as "Originator of Jazz." I am known by my nickname, which has a sexual reference, and due to the vulgarity of some of my music, many recordings were not released until the end of the twentieth century.

5. Name the three pin-up girls on Andy's cell wall in the movie *Shawshank Redemption*.

Name the pop singers with these recent hit songs:

6. "Hollaback Girl"

7. "Fall To Pieces"

8. "Since U Been Gone"

9. "Confessions of a Broken Heart"

10. "Genie In a Bottle"

Mystery Theme #4

----

1. In what movie did Al Pacino star as a not-gay bank robber?

2. At the beginning of *Cabaret*, this place was the setting (in Berlin).

3. What company's slogan was, "The dogs kid love to bite?"

4. What was the character name of the female lead (and Bond girl) in *Goldfinger*?

5. What is the name of the state flower and tree of Virginia? (Hint: It's the same for both.)

6. What is the nickname of the brightest star in the night sky?

7. He is the self-proclaimed greatest in his field. His real name is Duane Chapman, but his better-known nickname is what?

8. What is the name of the actress that is perhaps best known by her character name, Samantha Jones?

9. In the northern hemisphere, these usually occur between July and September.

10. Actor William Katt starred on TV as a teacher named Ralph Hinkley, but on that show he was known better as what?

Taglines #2

Name the movie to which these taglines are associated.

1. "The coast is toast."

2. "The strangest story ever conceived by man."

3. "Not every gift is a blessing."

4. "There's something about your first piece."

5. "Where were you in '62?"

6. "Have the time of your life."

7. "A crash course in the birds, the bees, and bikinis."

8. "Make your last breath count."

9. "This is the weekend they didn't play golf."

10. "They're here."

What's the Movie?

Below is a list actors and actresses. Your task is to name the movie they starred in. The lead actor isn't always given, but to help, the year of the film's release is listed.

1. William H. Macy, Glenn Close, Gary Oldman, and Harrison Ford (1997)

2. Clint Eastwood and Shirley Maclaine (1970)

3. Robert Redford, Faye Dunaway, Max Von Sydow, and Cliff Robertson (1975)

4. Hugh Grant, Kristin Scott Thomas, and Andie MacDowell (1994)

5. Chris Tucker, Gary Oldman, and Milla Jovovich (1997)

6. David Schwimmer and Anne Heche (1998)

7. Charles Bronson, Steve McQueen, Yul Brenner, and James Coburn (1960)

8. Charlie Sheen, Christopher Lloyd, D.B. Sweeney, and John Cusack (1988)

9. Sandra Bullock, Tate Donovan, and Anne Bancroft (1992)

10. Bebe Neuwirth, Matthew McConaughey, and Kate Hudson (2003)

Mystery Theme #5

1. What was the name of the 1995 movie that starred Brad Pitt and Morgan Freeman as detectives investigating a series of ritualistic murders?

2. In what movie does Tom Hank's character lose his girlfriend, played by Helen Hunt?

3. What it is the name of the builder of TV, movie, and children's toy fame that has a catchphrase, "Can we fix it?"

4. What is the capital of the Centennial State?

5. What is the nickname of singer Geri Halliwell?

6. The 2003 movie *Veronica Guerin*, which starred Cate Blanchett, was about what Irish drug dealer?

7. Who was the voice of the cartoon character Mr. Magoo?

8. What is the nickname of poker superstar Howard Lederer?

9. The Schutzstaffel were better known by what abbreviation?

10. What is the common name for the largest family of fish found in North America?

    Hint: The name is also used to describe small silvery fish.

Tagline #3

Name the movie to which these taglines are associated.

1. "They're not just getting rich, they're getting even."

2. "It's a deadly game of tag, and Cary Grant is it."

3. "Here comes the bride."

4. "His whole life was a million-to-one shot."

5. "They're young. They're in love. And they kill people."

6. "Love is in the hair."

7. "Every man dies, not every man really lives."

8. "The snobs against the slobs."

9. "Can two friends sleep together and still love each other in the morning?"

10. "All it takes is a little confidence."

Las Vegas—The Old and The New

1. The lights along the Las Vegas Strip were dimmed in 1995 out of respect for the death of what famous Las Vegas singer?

2. Who played Danny Ocean in the original (1960) version of the movie *Ocean's 11*?

3. What was the name of the 1995 film starring Elizabeth Berkley, with support from Gina Gershon?

4. What hotel was demolished to make way for the Wynn Hotel?

5. What hotel was demolished to make way for the Bellagio Hotel?

6. What hotel was demolished to make way for the Mandalay Bay Hotel?

7. What hotel was demolished to make way for the Venetian Hotel?

8. What hotel did mobster Bugsy Siegel open on December 26, 1946?

9. What was the name of the tremendous performer, known for his many voices, who had been named Las Vegas Entertainer of the Year, and who died an untimely death in May 2009?

10. Name the four most common names associated with Frank Sinatra and the "Rat Pack."

Mystery Theme #6

Your challenge is to list the ten movies described below. Very little information is provided; however, all ten movies are related by one theme.

1. James Bond film produced by Albert R. Broccoli in 1981.

2. The 1982 film with support from Brian Dennehy, Richard Crenna, and a very young David Caruso playing Deputy Mitch.

3. The 1984 film, set in the south, for which Sally Field won an Oscar.

4. Psycho thriller starring Rebecca De Mornay and Annabella Sciorra.

5. The 1995 film with five Oscar wins, and an amazing performance from Sophie Marceau as the princess.

6. The 1993 horror film remake with Gabrielle Anwar and Meg Tilly.

7. The 1983 comedy starring Steve Martin and Kathleen Turner.

8. The story of Christy Brown, performed by Daniel Day-Lewis.

9. The 1983 film directed by Brian De Palma, with a screenplay by Oliver Stone. Mary Elizabeth Mastrantonio plays the sister, Gina.

10. The 2002 film starring Kari Wuhrer as a sheriff and Scarlett Johansson as her daughter.

24. Last Lines #2

For each of the following, supply the movie from which the last line was uttered. A "helpful" hint is included.

1. "I do wish that we could chat longer, but I'm having an old friend for dinner."
   Hint: Classic evil noir

2. "The, uh, stuff that dreams are made of."
   Hint: It ain't a dame he's talkin' about.

3. "You finally really did it, you maniacs! You blew it up! Ah, damn you. God damn you all to hell!"
   Hint: Movie with the largest makeup budget in history.

4. "What did he just say?"
   "He said, there's a storm coming in."
   "I know!"
   Hint: He actually said, "Viene la tormenta."

5. "Roads? Where we're going we don't need roads."
   Hint: Apparently this kid could get in trouble even before he was born.

6. "You're still here? It's over! Go home. Go!"
   Hint: A person should not believe in an "ism," he should believe in himself. I quote John Lennon, "I don't believe in the Beatles, I just believe in me."

7. "Aw, ladies, come on. . . ."
   Hint: He had his share of Susan and Michelle.

8. "Welcome to Hollywood! What's your dream? Everybody comes here. This is Hollywood, the land of dreams. Some dreams come true; some don't, but keep on dreamin', this is Hollywood. Always time to dream, so keep on dreamin'."

   Hint: She walked off the street, into his life, and stole his heart.

9. "Hey dad, you wanna have a catch?"
   "I'd like that."

   Hint: A clue would be corny.

10. "You better bury Ned right. You better not cut up nor otherwise harm no whores, or I'll come back and kill every one of you sons of bitches."

    Hint: He didn't hack the man up; he shot him.

25

Ten Degrees of Separation

Fill in the actor/actress or movie to complete the chain linking Kevin Bacon to his wife, Kyra Sedgwick.

Kevin Bacon starred in *Hollow Man* (2000) with actress _____ who

starred in *Cocktail* (1988) with actor_____ who starred in

Taps (1981) with Sean Penn who starred in _____ (1993)

with Al Pacino, who made two movies _____ (1991) and

_____ (1986) with Michelle Pfeiffer who starred in the movie

_____ (1990) with actor _____ who

starred with actor_____ in *The Name of the Rose* (1986)

who starred with actor_____ in *Broken Arrow* (1996) who

starred in the movie _____ (1996) with Kyra Sedgwick.

ANSWERS

Quiz 1

Crocodiles and Alligators

1. Elton John

2. John Quincy Adams

3. Alligator pear

4. *Live and Let Die*

5. *Gator*

6. *Lake Placid*

7. Elvis

8. Crocodile tears

9. René Lacoste

10. Walkabout Creek

Quiz 2

Literature— the Classics

1. James Joyce
2. F. Scott Fitzgerald
3. Vladimir Nabokov
4. Aldous Huxley
5. William Faulkner
6. Joseph Heller
7. Kurt Vonnegut
8. Henry James
9. William Faulkner
10. William Golding
11. Ernest Hemingway
12. Joseph Conrad
13. Norman Mailer
14. Dashiell Hammett
15. Sinclair Lewis

Quiz 3

Fifteen Degrees of Separation

1. *Spaceballs*
2. Independence Day
3. Jeff Goldblum
4. *The Fly*
5. Brad Pitt
6. *Meet Joe Black*
7. Jodie Foster
8. *Maverick*
9. *Lethal Weapon*
10. Gene Hackman
11. *The Grifters*
12. *American Beauty*
13. Kevin Spacey
14. *Jackie Brown*
15. *Point of No Return*

Quiz 4

The Power of Three

1. Babe Ruth
2. Triads
3. *Harry Potter and the Prisoner of Azkaban*
4. Tom Selleck, Steve Guttenberg, and Ted Danson
5. Miami, Bermuda, and Puerto Rico
6. Curly Joe, Joe, and Shemp
7. Jose Carreras, Placido Domingo, and Luciano Pavarotti
8. Chevy Chase, Steve Martin, and Martin Short
9. Jefferson Davis, Stonewall Jackson, and Robert E. Lee
10. For every action there is an equal

Quiz 5
The Bond Bonus

1. *License to Kill*
2. *Goldfinger*
3. *From Russia with Love*
4. *For Your Eyes Only*
5. *Thunderball*
6. *On Her Majesty's Secret Service*
7. *Octopussy*
8. *Tomorrow Never Dies*
9. *The Man with the Golden Gun*
10. *You Only Live Twice*

Quiz 6

North American Geography

1. Mount McKinley
2. Death Valley
3. Utah
4. Colorado, New Mexico, Arizona, and Utah
5. Oregon, Nevada, Arizona, and Baja California (which is a Mexican state)
6. Quebec
7. Yukon and Rio Grande
8. The Bronx, Manhattan, Brooklyn, Queens, and Staten Island
9. Georgia
10. Lake Michigan

Quiz 7
Mystery Theme #1

1. Cherry Garcia
2. *Bananas*
3. Orange or Orangemen
4. Lime
5. *The Cocoanuts*
6. The Cranberries
7. Desserts
8. Mandarin
9. Persimmon
10. Papaya

The mystery theme is fruit.

Quiz 8

One-Hit Wonders #1

----

1. Dexy's Midnight Runners
2. C.W. McCall
3. Sir Mix-a-Lot
4. Men Without Hats
5. Baha Men
6. Bobby McFerrin
7. Sugarhill Gang
8. Taco
9. The Verve
10. Thomas Dolby

Quiz 9
One-Hit Wonders #2

1. The Vapors
2. Los Del Rio
3. Wild Cherry
4. Stacey Q
5. Nena
6. Gerardo
7. Vickie Sue Robinson
8. Norman Greenbaum
9. Haddaway
10. Nick Gilder

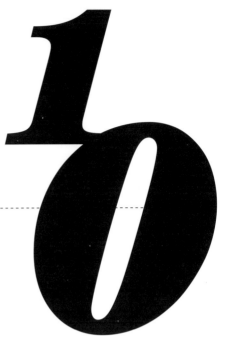

Quiz 10
Last Lines #1

1. *Magnum Force*
2. *Speed*
3. *The Ten Commandments*
4. *The Hustler*
5. *The Color of Money*
6. *My Fair Lady*
7. *Blazing Saddles*
8. *Stand By Me*
9. *Casablanca*
10. *Some Like it Hot*

Quiz 11
Mystery Theme #2

1. Liverpool
2. Ports
3. Mouth
4. W and BA
5. Chelsea
6. Arsenal
7. Newcastle
8. Bolton
9. West
10. Ham

The mystery theme is Premier League football (or soccer).

Quiz 12

Literature— The Readers' List

1. Ayn Rand
2. L. Ron Hubbard
3. Harper Lee
4. Robert Heinlein
5. Thomas Pynchon
6. Margaret Mitchell
7. Stephen King
8. John Fowles
9. Douglas Adams
10. John Irving
11. Ray Bradbury
12. Jack London
13. Richard Adams
14. Tom Clancy
15. Salman Rushdie

Quiz 13
Taglines #1

1. *The Blues Brothers*
2. *Spinal Tap*
3. *Ferris Bueller's Day Off*
4. *Platoon*
5. *Scarface*
6. *Jaws 2*
7. *X-Files*
8. *Mars Attacks*
9. *Psycho*
10. *Wayne's World*

Quiz 14
Mystery Theme #3

----

1. *The Transporter*
2. Q
3. *Bones*
4. Pete Dye
5. Lithium
6. Bjorn Borg
7. *Ten*
8. Forward
9. Quarks
10. *Voyager*

**The mystery theme is the world of
Star Trek.**

Quiz 15
Stars and Bars

1. The Regal Beagle
2. Vincent van Gogh
3. Gary's Old Time Tavern
4. Five: one large and four small
5. The Confederate flag
6. The Bronze
7. He only eats guitars
8. Rosie's
9. Gilley's
10. Two

Quiz 16

Pop Tarts and
Breakfast Snacks

----

1. 420 calories

2. True

3.   A. Kellogg's
      B. Quaker Oats
      C. Post
      D. General Mills
      E. General Mills

4. Jelly Roll Morton

5. Raquel Welch, Rita Hayworth, and Marilyn Monroe

6. Gwen Stefani

7. Avril Lavigne

8. Kelly Clarkson

9. Lindsay Lohan

10. Christina Aguilera

Quiz 17
Mystery Theme #4

----

1. *Dog Day Afternoon*
2. The Kit Kat Club
3. Oscar Meyer
4. Pussy Galore
5. Dogwood
6. Sirius or the dog star
7. *Dog the Bounty Hunter*
8. Kim Cattrall
9. The dog days of summer
10. *The Greatest American Hero*

The mystery theme is cats and dogs.

Quiz 18
Taglines #2

1. *Volcano*
2. *King Kong*
3. *The Sixth Sense*
4. *American Pie*
5. *American Graffiti*
6. *Dirty Dancing*
7. *How to Stuff a Wild Bikini*
8. *Scream*
9. *Deliverance*
10. *Poltergeist*

Quiz 19
What's the Movie?

1. *Air Force One*
2. *Two Mules for Sister Sara*
3. *Three Days of the Condor*
4. *Four Weddings and a Funeral*
5. *The Fifth Element*
6. *Six Days, Seven Nights*
7. *The Magnificent Seven*
8. *Eight Men Out*
9. *Love Potion #9*
10. *How To Lose a Guy in 10 Days*

Quiz 20
Mystery Theme #5

1. *Seven*
2. *Castaway*
3. Bob
4. Denver
5. Ginger Spice
6. John Gilligan
7. Jim Backus
8. The Professor
9. SS
10. Minnow

The mystery theme is Gilligan's Island.

QUIZZES

Quiz 21
Tagline #3

----

1. *Trading Places*
2. *North by Northwest*
3. *Kill Bill: Vol. 1*
4. *Rocky*
5. *Bonnie and Clyde*
6. *There's Something About Mary*
7. *Braveheart*
8. *Caddyshack*
9. *Sleepless in Seattle*
10. *The Sting*

Quiz 22

Las Vegas— the Old and the New

1. Dean Martin
2. Frank Sinatra
3. *Showgirls*
4. The Desert Inn
5. The Dunes
6. The Hacienda
7. The Sands
8. The Pink Flamingo Hotel
9. Danny Gans
10. Dean Martin, Sammy Davis, Jr., Joey Bishop, and Peter Lawford

Quiz 23
Mystery Theme #6

1. *For Your Eyes Only*
2. *First Blood*
3. *Places in the Heart*
4. *The Hand That Rocks the Cradle*
5. *Braveheart*
6. *Body Snatchers*
7. *The Man with Two Brains*
8. *My Left Foot*
9. *Scarface*
10. *Eight Legged Freaks*

Quiz 24
Last Lines #2

1. *Silence of the Lambs*
2. *Maltese Falcon*
3. *Planet of the Apes*
4. *Terminator*
5. *Back to the Future*
6. *Ferris Bueller's Day Off*
7. *The Witches of Eastwick*
8. *Pretty Woman*
9. *Field of Dreams*
10. *Butch Cassidy and the Sundance Kid*

Quiz 25

Ten Degrees of Separation

1. Elizabeth Shue
2. Tom Cruise
3. *Carlito's Way*
4. *Frankie* and *Johnny*
5. *Scarface*
6. *Russia House*
7. Sean Connery
8. Christian Slater
9. John Travolta
10. *Phenomenon*

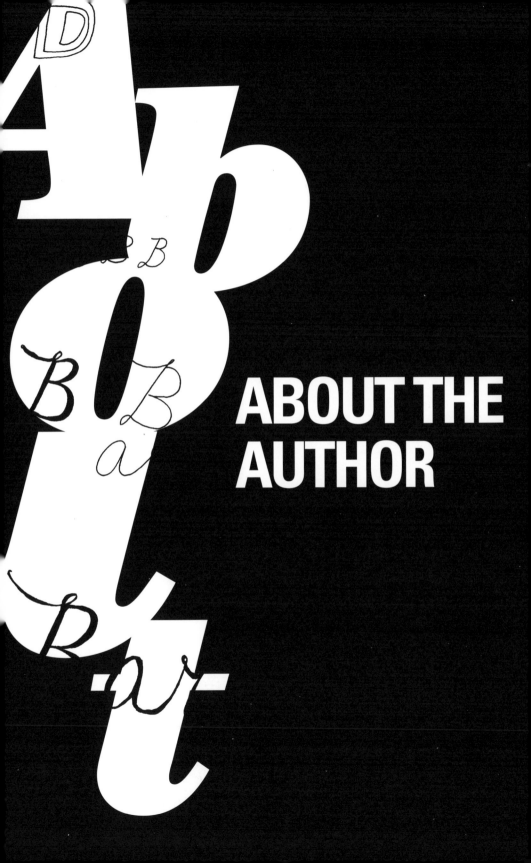

ABOUT THE
AUTHOR

Rick Saldin is the senior tax manager and financial planner at Bruno Financial in Westlake Village, California. He received his MBA from the University of Southern California. Prior to becoming a certified public accountant, he received a medical degree from the College of Podiatric Medicine, in San Francisco, California. Rick performs his bar Quiz every Monday night at the Crown and Anchor Pub in Thousand Oaks, California.

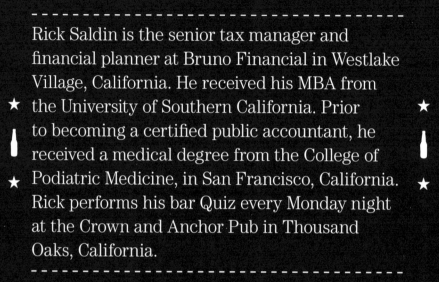

BAR

QUIZZES